F/A-18 Hornet

in action

by Lou Drendel

Color by Lou Drendel
Illustrated by Joe Sewell

Aircraft Number 136
squadron/signal publications

On 17 January 1991, the first day of Operation DESERT STORM, a pair of F/A-18C Hornets from VFA-81 shot down a pair of MiG-21s with AIM-7 missiles. Both kills were Beyond Visual Range (BVR) head on shots and the Hornets were able to continue on to bomb their target, an Iraqi airfield.

ISBN 0-89747-300-0

If you have any photographs of the aircraft, armor, soldiers or ships of any nation, particularly wartime snapshots, why not share them with us and help make Squadron/Signal's books all the more interesting and complete in the future. Any photograph sent to us will be copied and the original returned. The donor will be fully credited for any photos used. Please send them to:

Squadron/Signal Publications, Inc.
1115 Crowley Drive.
Carrollton, TX 75011-5010.

Photo Credits

McDonnell-Douglas
Ted Carlson
David Brown
Author's Collection

U.S. Navy
Dave Mason
Nick Waters
Graham Mansell

Foreward

F/A? — To those who are familiar with the pecking order of Naval Aviation, this designation seems like a step toward ultimate confusion. The professional and social distinctions between Navy fighter and attack pilots has fostered all sorts of interesting interservice by-play and rivalries. And this difference is not taken casually. It is a career long, even life long, vocational mind-set.

Unlike the Air Force, which considered its pilots qualified to fly everything from the O-1 to the B-52, the Navy had always respected the career paths chosen by its fledgling aviators. If you opted for the attack or fighter "communities" out of flight training, then you were more than likely an "attack puke" or "fighter puke" for the rest of your life. Not that fighter pilots didn't drop bombs. Hellcat, Panther, and Phantom pilots might have actually spent more time moving mud than they did chasing bandits. Even that epitome of the single-engine, single seat fighter, the F-8 was modified to carry air-to-ground munitions.

The introduction of the F-14 Tomcat polarized the two communities. The F-14 could not carry bombs, it was strictly a fighter/interceptor, possibly the best ever built. Now fighter pukes were really different from attack pukes. Slugging it out with ground targets was left to the A-6 and A-7, while the F-14's lived in top gun territory.

The complexities of modern jet aircraft dictated mission specialization until technology began to overtake the skills needed for air-to-air or air-to-ground combat. Now it became possible to build an aircraft that could do both missions. And so was born the F/A-18, or as it has sometimes been called in the Navy, the "F and A eighteen." This is the airplane which may create the ultimate schizoid personality...the melding of the attack and fighter puke! The Marines, of course, would be exempt. They have always considered their aircraft as a means of supporting the grunts, whether such support required dropping bombs or shooting down enemy aircraft. They institutionalized the split personality fighter squadron a long time ago; with the VMFA designation, which has been carried on Marine fighters since before the Vietnam War.

A pair of F/A-18 Hornets of Fighter/Attack Squadron Fifteen (VFA-15) Valions. Both aircraft are carrying centerline 330 gallon external fuel tanks, Blue painted practice bombs on horizontal ejector ranks on the inboard wing pylons and AIM-9 Sidewinders on the wingtips. (McDonnell-Douglas)

Introduction

The F/A-18 Hornet is the grandchild of the famous Northrop aircraft designer, Lee Begin. In 1966 Begin started work on his follow-on to the very successful F-5 Freedom Fighter. The F-5, designed in 1955, flew for the first time as the N-156C in 1959. It was ordered into production by the USAF in 1962. Intended from the beginning as a relatively cheap, lightweight fighter for U.S. allies, 2,610 F-5s were eventually produced in at least eighteen different versions, for over thirty different nations.

Begin's new fighter, which he christened the P-530, and which eventually earned the nickname "Cobra," bears a striking resemblance to the F/A-18. From the outset, it was intended to be a relatively lightweight, cheap, multi-purpose fighter, capable of dropping bombs or engaging enemy aircraft with equal proficiency. Unfortunately, there was no American market for such an aircraft at that time. The Navy was about to select the Grumman F-14 Tomcat as the winner of its competition to find a new carrier-based fighter-interceptor and the USAF was about to select the McDonnell Douglas F-15 Eagle as its new fighter. Both of these aircraft were big, heavy and designed solely for the purpose of air-to-air combat.

Since Northrop's experience with F-5 foreign sales had been so good, they turned their attention to optimising the P-530 for foreign use and license manufacture, or shared manufacture of various components. The Northrop marketing department persisted in their efforts to find a foreign customer, while the design development people continued to improve the basic design of the airplane. By 1971 Northrop had spent over $20 million of its own money in the project, and still had no customers to show for this investment.

That might have been the end of the line for the P-530, but for the efforts of the now-famous "Fighter Mafia" within the Pentagon. That small band of officers insisted that smaller, lighter and cheaper was the way to go in fighter design. The lightweight, cheap and maneuverable MiG-17s, 19s and 21s had acquitted themselves admirably in the skies over North Vietnam. No matter that the strategic and tactical decks had been heavily stacked against U.S. fighters, the fact was, the MiGs had just about fought the more sophisticated U.S. fighters to a draw. In the strict sense of dollars expended, the MiGs had won and dollars are often the way politicians keep score. Enter the lightweight fighter. The 1971 Pentagon budget contained funds for a pair of lightweight fighter prototypes, one of which would eventually be selected for production for USAF and foreign customers.

There were five contenders in this contest: Boeing, General Dynamics, LTV, Lockheed and Northrop submitted proposals. Northrop's proposal was the P-530, now upgraded to P-600 designation by the addition of General Electric YJ-101 turbofan engines of 15,000 lbs thrust. After a very thorough evaluation, the winners were announced on 13 April 1972. The General Dynamics and Northrop LWF designs were designated YF-16 and YF-17 respectively and each company was awarded a contract to build two prototypes.

The first YF-17 prototype (72-1569) rolled out on 4 April 1974 and made its first flight on 9 June 1974, with company test pilot Hank Chouteau at the controls. Number two first flew on 21 August 1974. Both YF-17 prototypes joined the YF-16 prototypes at Edwards AFB for evaluation. At this time, there was no Air Force contract contemplated and the first DOD and State Department meeting with the NATO consortium which would eventually provide a great deal of the production impetus, had just taken place.

Belgium, Denmark, Netherlands, and Norway had formed a Multinational Fighter Program Committee (MFPC) to study the possibilities for replacement of their F-104s and they spent a great deal of time studying the two American lightweight fighters, which

The forerunner of the F/A-18 Hornet was the Northrop YF-17 lightweight fighter prototype. The YF-17, which rolled out on 4 April 1974, was Northrop's entry into the LWF fly-off against the General Dymanics F-16. (Northrop)

were now called "Air Combat Fighters" (ACF) when USAF decided that they should be multi-role, air-to-air and air-to-ground fighters. On 11 September, the USAF announced that it would buy 650 of the winning prototypes and on 13 January 1975, it was announced that the YF-16 had won the fly-off.

This might have been the end of the line for the Northrop contender, except that the Europeans were not bound by the USAF decision and they continued to evaluate both the YF-17 and YF-16, as well as the P-530 (the original Northrop European submission), the Mirage F-1 and a special version of the Saab Viggen. The Navy was also studying a new fighter, the Naval Air Combat Fighter (NACF), which would eventually replace the A-7. Since the F-14 was in some trouble at the time because of cost over-runs and the threatened shutdown of the production line by Grumman, which was being held to a contract that guaranteed they would lose money, the Navy wanted to make sure that its new NACF was capable of performing in the air-to-air arena.

Grumman's financial problems were not the only thing that was causing the Navy to doubt the efficacy of building more Tomcats. The F-14's TF-30 engines, originally designed and built for the F-111, were the first afterburning turbofan engines. As such, they suffered many performance shortcomings which impacted the F-14's operational capabilities. The F-14 was, and is, a great aircraft design. With the proper engines, which it did not get until it had been in the fleet for over ten years, it is the best interceptor in the world. With the TF-30, it was just an average performer, with maintenance problems to boot. In 1973, the Navy wasn't just looking at an airplane to replace the A-7 and F-4, it was looking at a possible replacement for its brand-new F-14! The fighter branch of the Navy set forth requirements for a fixed-wing experimental fighter/attack (VFAX) aircraft. In June of 1974 requests for proposal were sent to General Dynamics, Northrop, McDonnell-Douglas, and three others, who never got a chance to put pencil to paper because Congress rescinded the VFAX RFPs in August, directing the Navy to choose its VFAX from the lightweight fighter contenders.

General Dynamics and Northrop already had their VFAX contenders flying. McDonnell-Douglas did not, but they had the advantage of a great deal of experience in the design and construction of Naval aircraft. The Congressional mandate seemed to eliminate McDonnell-Douglas from consideration, unless a collaboration, based on their expertise, combined with the existing LWF designs, could be forged.

The YF-16 was chosen by USAF, based in part on its longer range and use of the F-100 engine, which was in production for the F-15. It was not McDonnell-Douglas' choice. They favored the YF-17 and approached Northrop to act as a partner in the development of the YF-17. Northrop agreed to McDonnell-Douglas being prime contractor, probably because the P-530 had traveled a long and troubled road, rejected by a host of foreign users and the USAF. The VFAX, now NACF, seemed like the last chance and, having a partner like McDonnell-Douglas must have seemed like a great way to finally sell the design.

The YF-17 prototype carried Northrop Chief Test Pilot Hank Chouteau's name under the canopy rail in White and a Cobra logo on the nose in Black and White. (Ted Carlson/Fotodynamics)

Although it lost the LWF competition, the Northrop YF-17 became the basis for the F/A-18 Hornet. It carried a variety of paint schemes promoting it variously as the 'Cobra' (the proposed land-based foreign version) and the 'F/A-18 Prototype.' It ended it's flying career at the Northrop Corporation's Hawthorne California facility. (Ted Carlson/Fotodynamics)

5

Development

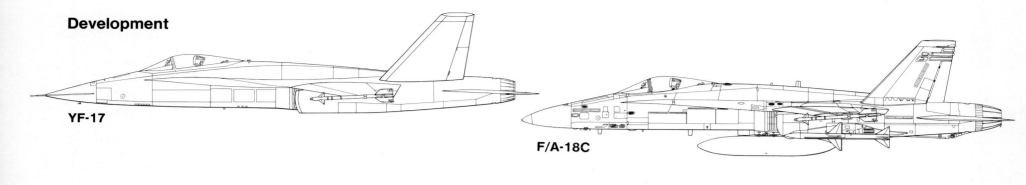

YF-17

F/A-18C

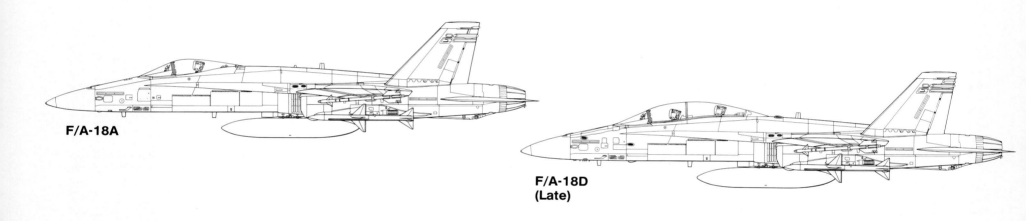

F/A-18A

**F/A-18D
(Late)**

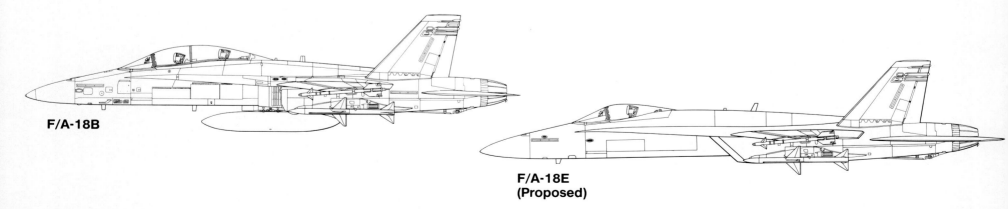

F/A-18B

**F/A-18E
(Proposed)**

F/A-18A Hornet

The U.S. Navy announced its choice for NACF as the McDonnell-Douglas Northrop design on 2 May 1975. Although visually similar, the F-18 Hornet, as the new design was christened, was not a modified version of the YF-17. It was quite similar in size and shape, but the task of navalising and multi-tasking of what had been designed as a land-based single-purpose technology demonstrator required a new design. Congress had dictated that the winning LWF design be developed as a multi-service airplane. General Dynamics collaborated with LTV to develop a carrier-based version of the F-16 and they expected it to be bought by the Navy. The wording of the Congressional mandate left room for argument that the Navy might choose from either of the LWF designs and, after examination of both, McDonnell-Douglas determined that the YF-17 was a better design for the NACF submission. After a lot of political in-fighting, the McDonnell-Douglas/Northrop partnership won their argument.

It was first thought that the Hornet would be built in two versions: F-18, optimized for air-to-air combat and A-18, for the attack mission. It very quickly became apparent, however, that the Hornet would have the capability to perform both tasks, so it was redesigned the F/A-18 (proof of this capability was demonstrated in Operation DESERT STORM, when a pair of VFA-81 Sunliners F/A-18Cs, each loaded with four Mk 84 2,000 pound bombs, two AIM-9 Sidewinders and two AIM-7 Sparrows engaged and shot down a pair of MiG-21s while enroute to targets in Iraq. In the Vietnam War, the appearance of MiGs often forced fighters to jettison their bombs before engaging the enemy).

The F/A-18A differed from the YF-17 in a number of ways. One of the most basic changes needed was the overall strengthening of the airframe to withstand the rigors of carrier operations. Radical redesign of the landing gear was necessary and this is perhaps the most noticeable of the many changes made in the basic YF-17 design. Other changes made included lengthening and widening of the fuselage to increase internal

fuel capacity from 5,500 pounds to 10,800 pounds, an increase in wing area from 350 to 400 square feet, a span reduction and shape change to the horizontal stabilators to accommodate carrier storage and enlarging the nose cone to accommodate a multimode radar.

The engines proposed for the F/A-18 were the experimental GE YJ-101 afterburning turbofans, which the Navy redesignated the F-404. General Electric was particularly anxious to make this engine successful, since Pratt & Whitney was already making engines for the F-14, F-15 and F-16. The F-404 engines installed in the Hornet have close to the same thrust as the General Electric J-79 engines which powered the F-4. That is where the similarity ends. The F-404 is half the weight, is one-third shorter, has forty percent fewer parts, is four times more reliable, can be installed on the either side of the Hornet, is smokeless, and has the same responsiveness as the J-79, although through a greater range of operation. The Hornet demonstrated better than 90 degrees angle of attack (AOA), with 45 degree angle of side slip. The J-79 was one of the great fighter engines of the jet age, but the newer F-404 showed how much the state of the art had advanced. The performance of the engines provided a significant improvement over the F-4 and A-7 which the F/A-18 would replace.

The F/A-18 also incorporated self-start capability with a turbine-driven auxiliary power unit (APU), which drives the air turbine starter on the airframe mounted accessory drive (AMAD) and, through a power take-off shaft, cranks the engine. On-board fire extinguishers allow the pilot to put out fires quickly. The fuel system has two self-sealing, independent feed tanks and self-sealing fuel lines which are contained within the tanks. The wing tanks have foam and there is foam in all fuselage voids. There are no fuel tanks between or around the engines and no electrical power is needed to transfer or feed fuel to the engines. Hydraulic fluid for the F/A-18 is non-flammable and it circulates through two completely separated systems, each of which has two independent branches. The system provides for automatic shut-down of any failed branch.

The structure of the F/A-18 incorporates multiple-spar wings and vertical tails and all control surfaces are redundant (this was demonstrated dramatically when a TF-18A

F/A-18A Evolution

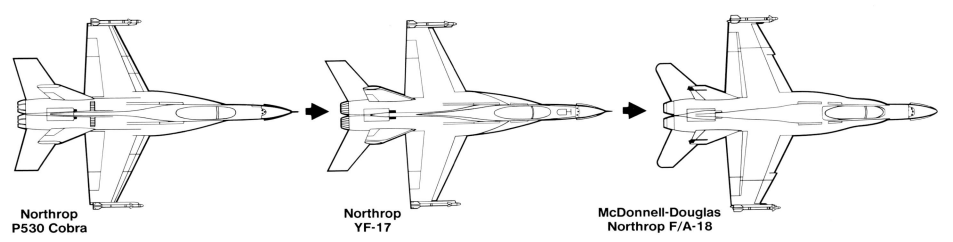

Northrop
P530 Cobra

Northrop
YF-17

McDonnell-Douglas
Northrop F/A-18

of USNTPS flew through trees at the departure end of the runway at NAS Patuxent River, removing the leading edge flaps, major portions of the trailing edge flaps and the entire port stabilator. The flight control computer compensated for the missing control surfaces, allowing the pilot to make one circuit and land safely). Fifty percent of the structural weight of the Hornet is aluminum, sixteen percent is steel, thirteen percent is titanium (including the firewall between the engines) and, although only nine percent of the weight is advanced graphite/epoxy, it covers forty percent of the surface areas. Use of graphite/epoxy in some of the most fatigue-prone areas, such as the speed brake, wing skins, trailing edge flaps, stabilators and vertical fins and rudders contributes to the high design service life of 6,000 hours.

Maintainability is an important aspect of combat aircraft design, since the successful performance of the mission may require quick turn-around and high in-service rates. The F/A-18 raised those standards to new levels, doubling the mean flight hours between failure compared to the F-4 and A-7, and reducing the maintenance man hours per flight hour to one-third that of the F-4 and one-half that of the A-7. The Hornet was designed with 307 access doors, ninety percent of which can be reached without the benefit of work stands. A single point maintenance monitor panel (MMP) in the nose wheel well gives a more detailed indication of the failure identifying the specific assembly that failed. The MMP also tells the ground crew if servicing of engine oil, hydraulics, LOX, radar coolant or fire extinguishing agents are necessary. The maintenance signal data recorder keeps track of all maintenance, which simplifies maintenance records-keeping. Other built in test (BIT) functions can be accessed by the pilot, using one of three CRTs in the cockpit, before and after each flight.

Aerodynamics and advanced engine technology gave the Hornet new capabilities, but the heart of the F/A-18 is the cockpit. The capability to carry a variety of weapons would lose its impact if the pilot was not able to use them effectively. Digital technology makes it possible to provide the Hornet pilot with more information than is available in both cockpits of the F-4, combined with the single cockpit of the A-7. Like other fighters of its generation, the primary information display is the Head-Up-Display (HUD) on the gunsight glass. The HUD displays airspeed, altitude, vertical speed, angle of attack, heading, Mach number, Gs and a variety of weapons delivery information. The older round barometric instruments are relegated to a backup role, located in a bottom corner of the panel.

Aircraft systems are monitored with the information displayed on three cathode ray tubes (CRTs) and managed with the twenty push buttons that surround each of these CRTs. The benefits of having all the necessary information within the pilots immediate field of view are reduced fatigue and a reduced susceptibility to vertigo. The preceding generations of fighter aircraft had dozens of controls and gages on the cockpit consoles and often required a pilot to look down, left, right or even slightly to the rear in order to read them.

The F/A-18 prototype during its first flight over St. Louis with test pilot Jack Krings at the controls. The F/A-18 prototype featured a 'sawtooth' wing leading edge, later eliminated on production aircraft. (McDonnell-Douglas)

The F/A-18A Hornet prototype made it's first flight on 18 November 1978 from the McDonnell-Douglas Aircraft headquarters at Lambert Field, St. Louis. The aircraft was painted overall White with Blue and Gold trim. (McDonnell-Douglas)

use them. This was a sure-fire recipe for vertigo when outside visual cues were not sharply defined.

All combat functions for air-to-air and air-to-ground attack can be operated from controls on the throttles and stick grip (Hands-On-Throttle-And-Stick or HOTAS has since become another standard of modern fighter design). The pilots ability to operate these controls without looking into the cockpit is the most critical combat skill. It has come to be known as 'playing the piccolo' by fighter pilots and requires frequent practice to maintain a combat edge.

The heart of the F/A-18's weapons system is the Hughes AN/APG-65 multimode pulse Doppler radar. The radar is operated in several modes, including Boresight, Vertical Acquisition and Head Up Display during air combat maneuvering (ACM). These modes feature automatic acquisition of maneuvering targets at ranges of 500 feet to five nautical miles. Another ACM mode is the Gun Director Mode, which is a special short-range track mode. The radar's high pulse repetition frequency (PRF) makes it very effective in long range tracking of nose aspect targets, giving velocity and azimuth information.

Range-While-Search uses high and medium PRF to detect all-aspect targets, and Track-While-Scan maintains ten target track files, displaying eight. When the Advanced Medium Range Air to Air Missile (AMRAAM) missile becomes operational, the F/A-18 will be able to simultaneously attack as many targets as it has missiles to shoot. The Raid Assessment feature of the radar allows the pilot to expand the region centered on a single tracked target, giving increased resolution in the target vicinity, which permits radar separation of closely spaced targets.

In the air-to-ground attack role, the APG-65 has a number of modes including: long range surface mapping which enhances target location and identification, navigation and weapons delivery. High resolution mapping, combined with additional modes of the radar, give the pilot the ability to detect and track fixed, moving and sea surface targets, as well as the ability to cue other sensors such as the Forward Looking Infrared (FLIR). A terrain avoidance mode is available for low-level night or bad weather penetration missions. A precision velocity update feature improves navigation accuracy by

automatically updating the inertial navigation platform. It also serves as the doppler input to weapons delivery computation. A sea surface search mode suppresses sea clutter by sampling the sea state and setting a threshold above that of sea clutter. Two-channel monopulse angle tracking and coherent frequency agility allows accurate tracking of ground fixed or moving targets, and air-to-surface ranging is provided by the radar through use of split-gate range tracking at large depression angles, or elevation mono-pulse tracking at small depression angles. Designation of the target provides automatic acquisition in this mode, and designation can also be provided by the laser spot tracker or by FLIR.

These capabilities are provided by a fully software programmable signal processor, which performs 7.2 million operations per second! The APG-65 is extremely reliable, having qualified for the 106 hours mean time between failure (MTBF) standards set by military test procedures. Shop replaceable assemblies, no scheduled maintenance reqire-ments, and the fact that no special maintenance tools are needed, make maintenance faster and easier for military technicians, which translates to a higher in-service rate for operational Hornet squadrons.

Although it is capable of carrying up to 17,000 pounds of ordnance, the F/A-18A was designed with only one internal weapon, a six-barrel 20MM Vulcan cannon. This was finally included in the Hornet after a lengthy battle between the combat aviators who suffered through the Vietnam War in F-4s without an internal gun and the engineers who were concerned about the 5,000 pounds of weight the gun, ammunition and gas required to carry it added to the basic airplane. The aviators finally prevailed, not only in having the gun added, but in having it placed where it would be most accurate and reliable; right on the centerline of the airplane, in the nose, right next to the radar. In so doing, they created some tough problems for the designers. The 20MM Vulcan is capable of firing up

The third FSD Hornet (BuNo 160777) was used for carrier suitability testing with the initial tests being conducted aboard USS AMERICA (CV-66), beginning on 30 October 1979. The final test series, which certified the automatic landing system, were conducted aboard USS CARL VINSON during in early 1982. (McDonnell-Douglas)

Fuselage Development

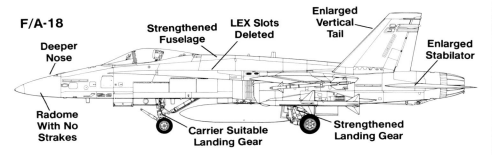

YF-17
- Test Probe
- Nose Strakes
- LEX Slots
- Lightweight Landing Gear

F/A-18
- Deeper Nose
- Radome With No Strakes
- Strengthened Fuselage
- LEX Slots Deleted
- Enlarged Vertical Tail
- Enlarged Stabilator
- Carrier Suitable Landing Gear
- Strengthened Landing Gear

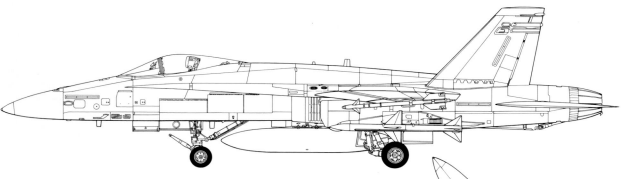

Specifications

McDonnell Douglas F/A-18A Hornet

Wingspan . . . . .37 feet 6 inches
Length . . . . .56 feet
Height . . . . .15 feet 3½ inches
Empty Weight . . . . .23, 050 pounds
Maximum Weight . . . . .49, 224 pounds
Powerplants. . . . . .Two 16, 000 lbst
                  GE F-404-GE-400

Armament. . . . . .One M-61 20MM cannon
                  Nine external weapons
                  stations

Performance
  Maximum Speed . . . . .1, 305 mph
  Service ceiling . . . . .50, 000 feet
  Range . . . . .2, 303 miles
Crew . . . . .One

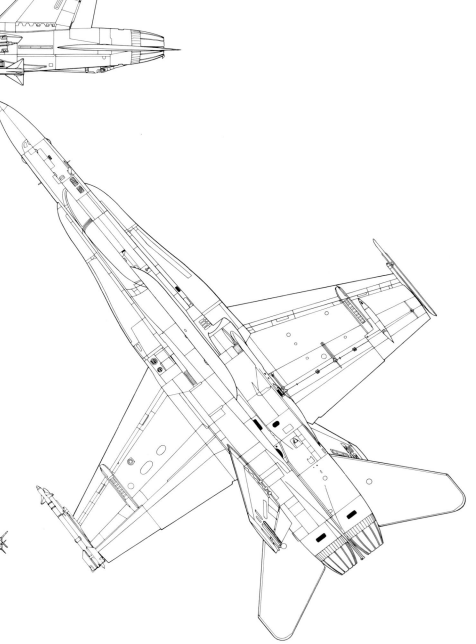

to 6,000 rounds per minute. This rate of fire causes vibration, generates a lot of heat, gas and smoke, all of which is harmful to the reliable operation of sophisticated radar. The radar compartment could be sealed to keep out gas and smoke and the cooling could be augmented, but dealing with the vibration was tougher. It required identification of the gun vibration frequencies, then building baffles to dampen out their effects on the radar.

The F/A-18A made its first flight on 18 November 1978, with McDonnell-Douglas chief test pilot Jack Krings at the controls. This flight was made from the McDonnell Aircraft facility at Lambert Field, St. Louis. The number one Hornet (BuNo 160775) was the first of nine single-seat full scale development aircraft, and two two-seat TF-18s to take part in the test program, which was conducted at the Naval Air Test Center, NAS Patuxent River, Maryland.

The test program, which lasted nearly four years, was one of the most extensive and trouble-plagued programs ever endured by the Navy. Much of the trouble was caused by the double digit inflation of the late 1970s, which caused inevitable cost over-runs and periodic Congressional outcries for cancellation of the entire F/A-18 program. The Hornet design overcame all the negatives though and the first operational Hornet squadron, VFA-125, was commissioned at NAS Lemoore, California on 13 November 1980, as the fleet readiness squadron or RAG. VFA-125 received its first production Hornet on 19 February 1981. The first operational Hornet squadron was VMFA-314, based at MCAS El Toro, California. The official conversion from F-4 Phantoms to F/A-18 Hornets took place on 7 January 1983. A total of 380 F/A-18As were built, including the nine RDT&E airplanes which were used in the test program.

Hornet number six (BuNo 160780) was used for high angle of attack and spin tests and was lost during one of these tests. The aircraft went out of control during a spin test and crashed into Chesapeake Bay. The test pilot, LT C.T. Brannon of VX-4, successfully ejected. (D.F. Brown)

The number four airframe was dedicated to structural flight test. The entire Hornet flight test program was carried out at Naval Air Test Center, NAS Patuxent River, Maryland. (D.F. Brown)

Painted in International Orange and White, Hornet number six was also used to test the air refueling system, The aircraft refueled from a number of tankers including the KA-3B Skywarrior tanker. (McDonnell-Douglas)

F/A-18A BuNO 160782 was the eighth airframe built and was used for armament testing. It was the first Hornet to fire the M61 Vulcan cannon and launch an AIM-7 Sparrow. Additionally, it was the first Hornet to feature a straight wing leading edge. (D.F. Brown)

This F/A-18A of Strike Test Directorate at NATC carries several camera pods under the wingtips to record bomb separation. The Black and White markings on fuselage are an aid to measurement of relative motion in the films. (D.F. Brown)

Some of the prototypes continued to be used in various test programs long after the Hornet had reached the fleet. The number four ship was used to test themoplastic and carbon-epoxy composites in wing panel construction during August of 1988. (McDonnell-Douglas)

An F/A-18A Hornet of Fighter Attack Squadron (VFA-106) Gladiators, the east coast training squadron for new Hornet pilots, returns to base from a training mission over the bombing range in Central Florida during 1987. The aircraft carries a Multiple Ejector Rack (MER) on the outboard pylon.(Author)

This F/A-18A Hornet (BuNo 161214) served as the prototype for the reconnaissance conversion intended for the F/A-18C. The pallet mounted camera installation replaced the M61 Vulcan cannon in the nose and bulged camera doors replaced the gun compartment doors. (D.F. Brown)

Wing/Horizontal Stabilizer

F/A-18A (Early)

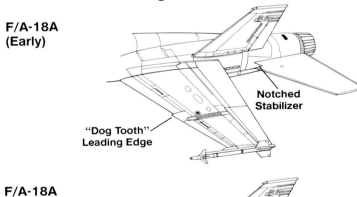

Notched Stabilizer

"Dog Tooth" Leading Edge

F/A-18A (Late)

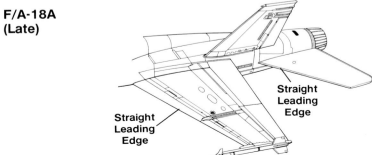

Straight Leading Edge

Straight Leading Edge

Purple Shirts (fuels personnel) refueling an F/A-18A Hornet of VFA-113 aboard USS CONSTELLATION, during the Hornet's first at sea deployment on 26 March 1985. The Hornet has a single point high pressure fueling system. (Navy)

F/A-18B

Two of the eleven research, development, test and evaluation (RDT&E) F/A-18 Hornets were built as two seat variants (BuNo 160781 and 160784). The initial designation of these and the forty production two seaters was TF-18A, however, this was later changed to F/A-18B.

The F/A-18B has the same overall length as the F/A-18A and to make room for the second cockpit, internal fuel capacity was reduced by some six percent. The F/A-18B is a dual-control fully combat capable trainer capable of carrying all of the same weapons as the single seat F/A-18A. All of the Navy and Marine squadrons which operated the F/A-18A had F/A-18Bs on strength for proficiency training purposes.

The first two-seat trainer variant was designated the TF-18A. It was the seventh Hornet manufactured and was used to validate the flying qualities of the two seat configuration. (D.F. Brown)

The number one two seat trainer was painted in overall White with Blue and Gold trim. The stripe on the fin is not a number, but rather a strip formation light. The aircraft carried the Hornet and number T1 on the nose in Black. (McDonnell-Douglas)

Fuselage Development

F/A-18A

Single Cockpit

TF-18A F/A-18B

Enlarged Single Piece Canopy

Second Cockpit

The TF-18A trainer was redesignated as the F/A-18B before the aircraft went into production. The F/A-18B is fully combat capable and can carry the same weapons as the single seat F/A-18A. This F/A-18B was assigned to the U.S. Navy Test Pilot School (USNTPS) at NAS Patuxent River. (D.F. Brown)

An F/A-18B (BuNo 161740) GD 03 of VAQ-34 on final approach for landing at NAS Miramar, California on 26 September 1992. VAQ-34 uses their F/A-18Bs in much the same manner as their earlier EA-4J, as electronic aggressors with pods carried on the wing pylons that simulate enemy radars. (Ted Carlson/Fotodynamics)

15

F/A-18C

The advanced F/A-18C made its first flight on 3 September 1986, from Lambert Field, St. Louis, with McDonnell-Douglas test pilot Glen Larson at the controls. The F/A-18C was the culmination of an improvement program aimed at making significant improvements to the basic F/A-18A. The prototype was delivered to NAS Patuxent River for testing and the first production F/A-18C was delivered just a year later. Although the only external changes are the addition of several new antennas, the capabilities of the Hornet were upgraded by giving the aircraft the capability of launching the AIM-120 AMRAAM and the IR imaging AGM-65 Maverick.

The F/A-18C was also equipped with the AKY-14 (XN-6) Mission Computer, which has increased memory (twice as much as its predecessor) and a faster processor. Mission information is stored on cassettes for easier and faster computer access. In 1990, Hughes Aircraft began work on an upgrade of the APG-65 radar, under a $223 million full scale development contract. The new radar, designated APG-73, had three times the speed and memory of the APG-65 and was to be installed in new production Hornets beginning in 1994. Additionally, the new radar could be retrofitted on all F/A-18C/D aircraft.

The F/A-18C uses the Navy Air Common Escape System (NACES), embodied in the Martin Baker ejection seat and associated survival equipment (NACES is the Navy's attempt at standardizing all ejection seats used in Naval aircraft). For electronic self-protection the Hornet carries an ALQ-165 jammer (although the Pentagon recently announced that budgetary constraints have forced cancellation of the AN/ALQ-165 ASPJ program, leaving F-14D and F/A-18C/Ds without internal ECM protection.)

The F/A-18C also has the capability of replacing the M61 Vulcan cannon with a pallet mounted reconnaissance system. The pallet mounted gun and external gun compartment doors are removed and replaced by the camera system and bulged camera compartment doors that contain the camera windows. A fairing over the gun port completes the conversion.

From 1989 onward, production Hornets were delivered with night attack capability provided by GEC Avionics night vision goggles (NVGs), which work by amplifying moonlight, starlight and/or reflected light from ground sources. The Hughes AAR-50 FLIR, contained in the thermal imaging navigation set (TINS) pod, is linked to a Kaiser HUD. NVG compatible cockpit displays provide the subdued instrument lighting necessary to maintain the effectiveness of the NVG goggles. Information from multi-function displays and a color digital moving map display are stored on a laser disk to provide mission intelligence information.

F/A-18C and two seat F/A-18D Hornets are equipped with a flight incident recorder and monitoring set (FIRAMS) ... commonly known as "the black box." The FIRAMS is linked with an integrated fuel and engine indicator and a data storage set for recording maintenance and flight incidents data. A signal data processor interfaces with the fuel system to provide overall system control, and enhanced built-in test (BIT) capability and automatic center-of-gravity adjustment as fuel is consumed.

Beginning in 1988, production Hornets were delivered with a "LEX Fence" installed on the top of both wing leading edge extensions (LEX). The LEX Fence is a thirty-two inch long by eight inch high piece of metal which reduces fatigue on the vertical tails and increases the service life of the F/A-18. LEX Fences have been retrofitted to all Hornets remaining in service. The LEX Fence was developed after cracks were found in the vertical fins of F/A-18A/B aircraft. The cracks were caused by the LEX vortices created by high AOA maneuvers. Since the Hornet lives at high AOA in combat, a fix was critical to its continued service and an eight month test program was conducted to find the proper shape, size, and placement of the LEX Fences.

An F/A-18C (BuNo 163481) of VFA-83 on final at Nellis AFB, Nevada on 1 April 1989. Externally the F/A-18C is nearly identical to the earlier F/A-18A except for a number of antennas (mainly around the nose section). (Ted Carlson/Fotodynamics)

In 1992, F/A-18C/Ds on the production line were re-engined with the more powerful General Electric F-404-GE-402 engines, which has twenty percent more thrust than the original F-404-GE-400 engines used on earlier Hornets. The first production Hornets with the new engines were export models for Kuwait which were delivered during early 1992.

Other avionics installed in the F/A-18C include: a Collins AN/ARN-118 TACAN, AN/ARC-182 UHF/VHF comm and DF-301E UHF/DF, Magnavox AN/ALR-50 and Litton AN/ALR-67 Radar Warning Receivers, GEC Ferranti Type 117 laser designator, Goodyear AN/ALE-39 Chaff Dispenser, Sanders AN/ALQ-126B ECM, Harris AN/ASW-25 radio data link, Eaton AN/ARA-63 receiver-decoder, GEC Ferranti FID 2035 horizontal situation indicator (HSI), Bendix/King HIS, J.E.T. ID-1791/A flight director indicator, ITT/Westinghouse AN/ALQ-165 airborne self protection jammer (ASPJ), Litton AN/ASN-130A inertial navigation system plus GPS. Displays are on Kaiser multifunction CRTs and GEC Ferranti-Bendix/King CRT and Kaiser AN/AVQ-28 HUD.

Performance of the F/A-18C includes a maximum speed of Mach 1.8 plus, an approach speed of 134 Knots, a combat ceiling of 50,000 feet, a combat radius of 290 nautical miles and an unrefuelled ferry range (with external tanks) of 1,800 nautical miles.

Antenna Configuration

F/A-18A

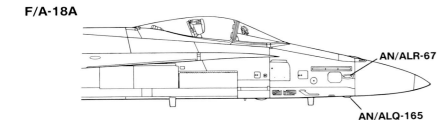

AN/ALR-67

AN/ALQ-165

F/A-18C

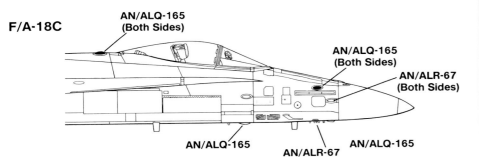

AN/ALQ-165 (Both Sides)

AN/ALQ-165 (Both Sides)

AN/ALR-67 (Both Sides)

AN/ALQ-165

AN/ALR-67

AN/ALQ-165

A pair of F/A-18Cs of VX-4 on a low level pass at NAS Point Mugu, California on 10 October 1992. Both of these aircraft have been fitted with the LEX fence on the leading edge extension just forward of the wingroot. (Ted Carlson/Fotodynamics)

The twin AN/ALQ-165 blisters on the sfuselage spine identify this as an F/A-18C (BuNo 163475) The aircraft was assigned to VFA-83 at NAS Miramar and was engaged in Top Gun training on 19 January 1989. The Rampagers were assigned to CVW-17, aboard USS SARATOGA. (Ted Carlson/Fotodynamics)

17

An F/A-18C Hornet (BuNo 163437) of VFA-86 Sidewinders on the transient ramp at NAS Miramar, California on 5 December 1992. This is the squadron commanders aircraft and it has all markings and lettering in Black (Ted Carlson/Fotodynamics

The Marine Hornet training squadron is VMFAT-101 based at MCAS El Toro, California. This F/A-18C (BuNo 164257) on final for landing at MCAS El Toro on 23 April 1992 has the fin flash and tail code in Black. (Ted Carlson/Fotodynamics)

Reconnaissance Conversion

F/A-18C

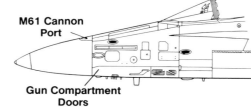

M61 Cannon Port

Gun Compartment Doors

F/A-18C

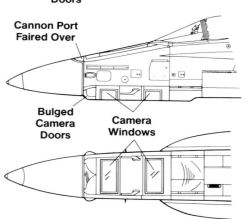

Cannon Port Faired Over

Bulged Camera Doors

Camera Windows

F/A-18D

The F/A-18D began life as a two seat, dual-control, combat capable proficiency trainer variant of the F/A-18C, but it quickly established an identity of its own with the introduction of night attack modifications.

While Navy variants of the F/A-18D retain dual controls in the rear cockpit, Marines F/A-18Ds have a dedicated all weather/night attack cockpit for use by a Weapons Systems Officer (WSO). The second set of controls was removed and a night attack weapon system was added with hand controllers on both consoles in the rear cockpit. The Marines plan to operate six squadrons of F/A-18Ds for the night/all weather attack mission. Additionally they will also replace their RF-4B reconnaissance aircraft with F/A-18Ds by using the aircraft's all-weather capability in conjunction with the Martin Marietta Advanced Tactical Airborne Reconnaissance System (ATARS) centerline pod containing a Loral AN/UPD-8 high resolution synthetic aperture side-looking-radar (SLAR) which supplements pallet mounted optical and infrared systems in the nose. Reconnaissance images can be transmitted in real-time, using datalink previously tested in Marines RF-4B recce Phantoms.

The Marines will also use the F/A-18D to replace the OA-4M Skyhawk in the Fast FAC role and some of their A-6 all-weather attack squadrons since cancellation of the A-12 program has resulted in a shortage of night/all-weather attack aircraft.

An F/A-18D (BuNo 164651) Night Attack Hornet of VMFA(AW)-225 Vikings on final for landing at MCAS El Toro on 24 April 1992. The squadron was reactivated on 1 July 1991 and got its first Hornets in February of 1992. (Ted Carlson/Fotodynamics)

The first production F/A-18D Night Attack Hornet made its first flight from St. Louis on 6 May 1988, carrying a Hughes AN/AAR-50 Thermal Imaging Navigation System (TINS) pod on the starboard fuselage station. The logo Night Attack was carried on both sides in Black. (McDonnell-Douglas)

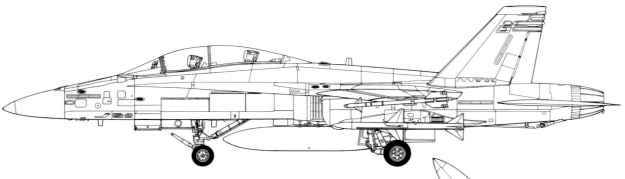

Specifications

McDonnell Douglas F/A-18D (Late) Hornet

Wingspan	37 feet 6 inches
Length	56 feet
Height	15 feet 3½ inches
Empty Weight	23, 050 pounds
Maximum Weight	49, 224 pounds
Powerplants	Two 19, 200 lbst GE F-404-GE-402
Armament	One M-61 20мм cannon Nine external weapons stations

Performance
Maximum Speed	1, 305 mph
Service ceiling	50, 000 feet
Range	2, 303 miles
Crew	One

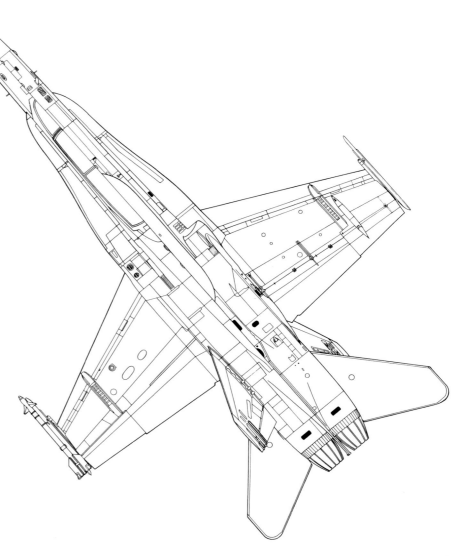

When Iraqi forces set fire to the Kuwait oil fields, the burning fires poured tons of Black oily smoke into the air, turning day into night. Under these conditions, the sensors on the night attack F/A-18Ds of VMFA(AW)-121 became even more valuable. (USMC)

This F/A-18D of VMFA (AW)-121 (BuNo 164051) suffered a surface-to-air missile hit in the afterburner cans but returned safely to base. Maintenance personnel had the Night Attack Hornet operational again within forty-eight hours. (D.F. Brown)

F/A-18E/F

The Hornet was designed from the outset for future growth as new systems became available. The first series of upgrades (F/A-18C/D) encompassed avionics and computer software improvements which enhanced the Hornets ability to attack at night in all weather conditions. The Hornet is compatible with more ordnance than any other aircraft in the U.S. inventory and can carry every air-launched weapon in development for the Navy. But there is a limit to how much you can squeeze into the existing package and the F/A-18C/D was close to that limit.

As a result, Mcdonnell-Douglas began development of an improved Hornet during 1983. The first company studies were aimed at increasing the internal fuel capacity of the Hornet. These studies languished until 1987, when then Secretary of Defense Caspar Weinberger challenged McDonnell-Douglas and General Dynamics to come up with significantly enhanced versions of the F/A-18 and the F-16 to fill what he perceived as gap in tactical capability in the late 1990s, prior to introduction of the next generation of combat aircraft (the Advanced Tactical Aircraft, ATA/A-12 for the Navy and the Advanced Tactical Fighter, ATF/YF-22) for the USAF).

The Naval Air Systems Command, with assistance from the Center for Naval Analysis and McDonnell-Douglas conducted the Hornet Upgrade study, also known as the "Hornet 2000." This study focused on four options for increasing the capability of the Hornet. The first option was a weapons system upgrade, which included software changes and survivability enhancements. These were ultimately added to the F/A-18C/D in the form of the APG-73 radar and the Airborne Self Protection Jammer (ASPJ). The second option included option one, plus addition of internal fuel capacity and a strengthened wing for more range and payload. Option three included one and two plus a larger wing (more chord and span), lengthened fuselage, and more weapons systems upgrades. The fourth option was much more radical, calling for a delta wing design with forward canards.

While added capability is always desirable and new programs are healthy for the system in general, the Navy was in a bind on Hornet 2000. It would force them to spend money that they did not have in the budget and an enhanced Hornet might well steal funds from the ATA, which was expected to be to the Navy what the F-117 and B-2 were to the Air Force. The Navy thought some of the money problems might be solved by getting a foreign partner to invest in the Hornet 2000 and a team of Navy and DOD officials made presentations to several European officials in 1988. They were up against the European Fighter Aircraft (EFA) and Dassault-Breguet Raphael, both state-of-the-art technology demonstrators. Politics and national pride aside, the Hornet seemed to make more sense for the Europeans, since it would cost roughly half of what the operational EFA or Raphael would cost. The program proposed 250 aircraft each for Britain and West Germany, 165 for Italy, 100 for Spain and 500 for the U.S. Navy. Projected follow-on sales included 100 for Canada, 150 for Greece, 25 for Portugal, 419 to Middle East countries, 200 to Asian countries and a further 300 for the Navy. The Europeans demurred, stating concerns that adoption of the Hornet 2000 would cost them much of their in-house development capabilities, and that the initial costs were still too high and the sales projections were far too optimistic.

The cancellation of the A-12 program forced the Navy to move ahead on the Hornet 2000. In July of 1991, Secretary of Defense Dick Cheney wrote: "The modernization of Naval Aviation must be bounded by affordability. In selecting the F/A-18E/F, we considered not only performance and unit price, but also a host of other factors which impact on cost. In the final analysis, the F/A-18E/F was the clear choice." The $3.715 billion development contract for the F/A-18E/F was finalized in late 1992. Referred to as "the definitized contract," it was a final, negotiated version of the letter contract awarded to McDonnell-Douglas the previous July. The cost-plus incentive contract covered seven and a half years of engineering and support activities, including manufacture and testing of seven flight test aircraft and three ground test articles. Northrop remained the principle subcontractor for the F/A-18E/F, while Hughes continued to build the radars and General Electric the engines. First flight of the E/F was projected for 1995.

The "E/F" suffix might lead one to believe that this is merely another variant of an existing aircraft aircraft. If you are trying to sell your program to Congress, that is a nice assumption for them to make. Following the July, 1992 contract award, the DOD Deputy Inspector General protested that the E/F had been approved without a full review. He asserted that "the F/A-18E/F will not merely be a modification of an existing aircraft, but rather a very different aircraft." He noted that only 15% of the C/D airframe would be compatible with the E/F, that the wing was totally redesigned and that the engines would also be new. He concluded his argument by stating that the E/F should be subject to the more stringent Milestone 2 documentation requirements of new systems procurement. In fact, the E/F had undergone a quite thorough testing in computer modeling and wind-tunnel testing, and the projections made for it were thought to be on the conservative side. The House Armed Services Committee, chaired by Les Aspin, who would be picked by President Clinton as the new Secretary of Defense, favored slowing spending on the E/F in favor of the AX, which was the follow-on attempt at coming up with a new medium Navy attack bomber to replace the cancelled A-12.

Although it is similar in appearance to earlier Hornets, the F/A-18E/F is a greatly improved aircraft. Structural changes to the airframe will increase internal fuel capacity by 33% over the C/D versions. The wings will have an additional 100 square feet, which will provide two additional hard points, improve flight characteristics, and allow 50% more payload to be brought back aboard ship. Advanced versions of the F404 engines will provide 35% more thrust, improving subsonic, transonic and supersonic performance. The new engines are designated F414 and are in the 22,000 pounds thrust range.

While the avionics will be 90% compatible with the C/D versions of the Hornet, improvements in the crew station will enhance these capabilities. Changes include a larger tactical situation display and a touchscreen up-front display. There are growth provisions such as improved cooling, increased electrical and hydraulic capacity, and more internal spaces for avionics, which will allow countering of any adversary threat by addition of more countermeasures and/or attack capabilities.

The major external differences between the proposed F/A-18E/F and earlier Hornets are the enlarged, rectangular intakes, additional wing pylons, increased area wing and stretched longer fuselage. (McDonnell-Douglas)

Exports

Although foreign sales have fallen far short of what Northrop had in mind when they designed the P-530 and went into partnership with McDonnell-Douglas in hopes of selling thousands of F-18L export fighters, the F/A-18 was chosen by several foreign governments and it is still on the market, while its chief rival, the F-16 will soon be going out of production.

Canada

The first foreign sale was to Canada, which announced that the Hornet was the winner of the New Fighter Aircraft (NFA) competition on 10 April 1980. The CF-18 replaced the CF-101 Voodoo in the NORAD air defense role, the CF-104 Starfighter in the air superiority role and the CF-5 in the close support and interdiction role, providing Canadian Forces with more capability in all three missions. Canada purchased ninety-eight CF-18As and forty CF-18Bs. The first flight of the CF-18 was on 29 July 1982 and all aircraft were delivered by September of 1988. Canadian Hornet units are: No 410 Operational Conversion Unit, No 416 Squadron and No 441 Squadron at CFB Cold Lake, Alberta, Nos 425 and 433 Squadrons at Bagotville, Quebec and Nos 439 and 421 Squadrons of the First Air Division at Baden Sollingen, Germany.

Canadian Hornets differ from Navy/Marine Hornets in that they are equipped with a civil ILS system, they also have a spotlight installed on the left side of the nose for air defense visual identification at night, and have provision for LAU-5003 nineteen shot rocket pods housing CRV-7 70mm high velocity sub-munition rockets.

A CF-18B (188932) of No 416 Squadron, Canadian Armed Forces on the transit ramp at George AFB, California on 28 March 1992. Canadian Hornets carry a powerful searchlight mounted in the port side of the nose for the identification of aircraft at night. (Ted Carlson/Fotodynamics)

A pair of CF-18A Hornets of No 410 Squadron on the ramp at Canadian Forces Base Cold Lake, Alberta during September of 1984. CFB Cold Lake is the site of the CAF weapons training range (similar to the USAF's Nellis AFB facility). (Tom Hildreth)

Australia

On 20 October 1981, the Royal Australian Air Force announced that it would purchase seventy-five Hornets (fifty-seven F/A-18As and eighteen F/A-18Bs). Designated the AF-18A and ATF-18A, the Australians opted for the Hornet due in large part to the manufacturing offsets in the agreement, which called for assembly of F/A-18s in Australia, first with U.S. manufactured parts, then from Australian manufactured components. The first two aircraft (MD built) were delivered to RAAF Williamtown on 17 May 1985. The first Australian-assembled Hornet made its first flight on 26 February 1985 and the first Australian manufactured AF-18 (Serial No A21-104) first flew on 3 June 1985.

AF-18s replaced the Mirage IIIO in No 2 Operational Conversion Unit, No 3 Squadron and No 77 Squadron all at RAAF Williamtown and No 75 Squadron at Tindal. RAAF Hornets are configured to carry the AGM-88 HARM, AGM-84 Harpoon and 2,000 pound Laser Guided Bombs (LGBs). They have been retrofitted with F/A-18C/D avionics, including LORAL AN/ASS-38 infrared tracking and laser designating pod.

Spain

On 30 May 1983, Spain announced the winner of the *Futuro Avion de Combate y Ataque* program was the F/A-18, redesignated C.15 and CE.15 (for Caza or Fighter and Caza Entrenamiento or Fighter Trainer). A total of seventy-two Hornets were purchased (twelve CE.15s and sixty C.15s) delivered in batches of eleven, twenty-six, fifteen, twelve and eight from 1986 to 1990. The first flight of a Spanish Hornet was on 4 December 1985. Spanish operational squadrons include: No 151 and 152 Squadrons of Ala de Caza 15 at Zaragoza and No 121 and 122 Squadrons of Ala de Caza 12 at Torrejon.

A pair of CF-18As (188785 and 188793) of No 433 Squadron depart Nellis AFB on 23 March 1988. Canadian Hornets carry a false canopy painted on the underside of the nose. This is carried as a possible way to confuse an enemy in a turning fight. It also can make it real hard for your wingman to rejoin! (Ted Carlson/Fotodynamics)

Kuwait

The first of forty (thirty-two F/A-18Cs and eight F/A-18Ds) Hornets for Kuwait was delivered in ceremonies at McDonnell-Aircraft in St. Louis on 8 October 1991. It was the first Hornet powered by the newer, more powerful F-404-GE-402 Enhanced Performance Engines (EPE). Development of the Kuwaiti Hornets was not delayed by the Iraqi invasion of Kuwait in 1990 and deliveries are scheduled to be completed during 1993. The Kuwaiti Hornets will replace their twenty year-old A-4 Skyhawks.

Switzerland

On 19 December 1991, the Swiss government's Federal Council formally submitted a $2.6 billion acquisition bill to the Swiss Parliament for the purchase of thirty-four F/A-18s. This followed an extensive evaluation program, dating from 1988, in which the Swiss looked at the F-16, JAS-39 and Mirage 2000-5. This evaluation, known as the *Neue Jagdflugzeug* competition was aimed at finding a replacement for the Northrop F-5E in Swiss service. Deliveries are expected to commence in 1995.

Finland

On 6 May 1992 the Government of Finland announced that the F/A-18 had won its DX fighter competition. Finland plans to purchase sixty-four Hornets, with the first seven F/A-18Ds assembled in St. Louis and the remaining fifty-seven F/A-18Cs assembled by Valmet Aviation Inc. in Halli, Finland. Deliveries are scheduled to begin in 1995 and run through 2000. The Hornet won the evaluation over the JAS-39 Gripen, Mirage 2000-5 and the MiG-29. The Hornets will replace the SAAB J35 Draken and MiG-21s in the air defense role.

Searchlight Installation

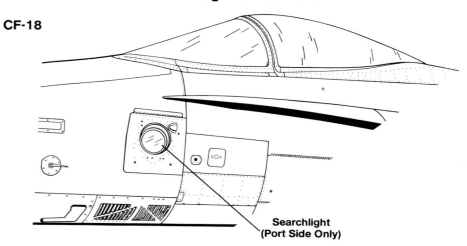

CF-18

Searchlight
(Port Side Only)

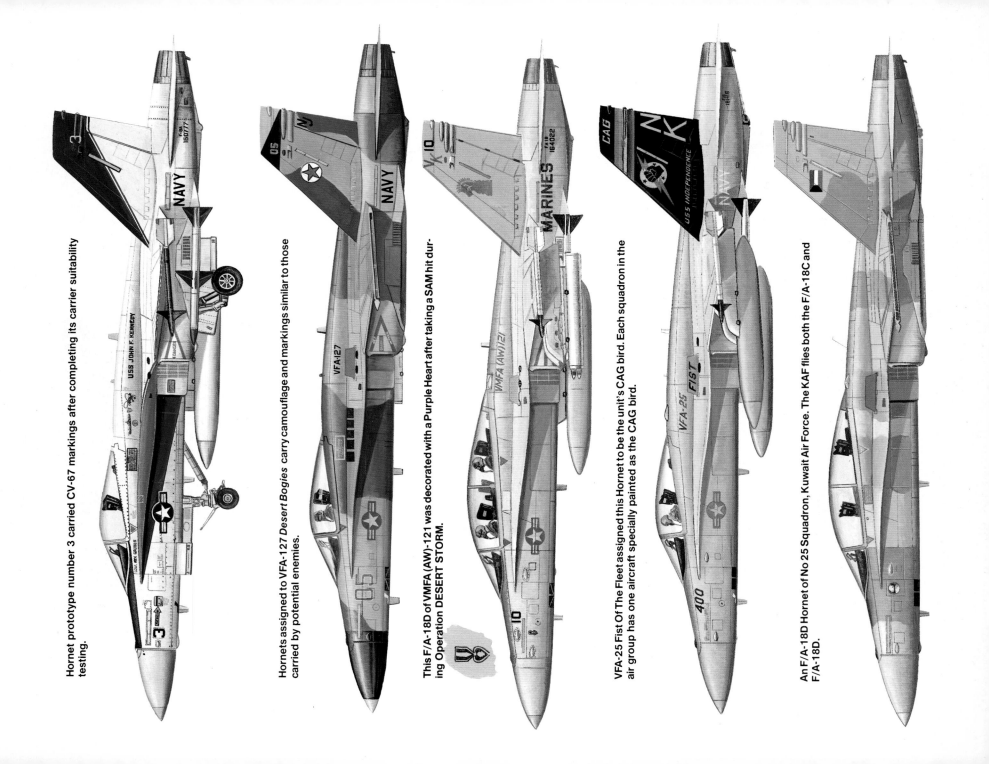

Hornet prototype number 3 carried CV-67 markings after completing its carrier suitability testing.

Hornets assigned to VFA-127 *Desert Bogies* carry camouflage and markings similar to those carried by potential enemies.

This F/A-18D of VMFA (AW)-121 was decorated with a Purple Heart after taking a SAM hit during Operation DESERT STORM.

VFA-25 Fist Of The Fleet assigned this Hornet to be the unit's CAG bird. Each squadron in the air group has one aircraft specially painted as the CAG bird.

An F/A-18D Hornet of No 25 Squadron, Kuwait Air Force. The KAF flies both the F/A-18C and F/A-18D.

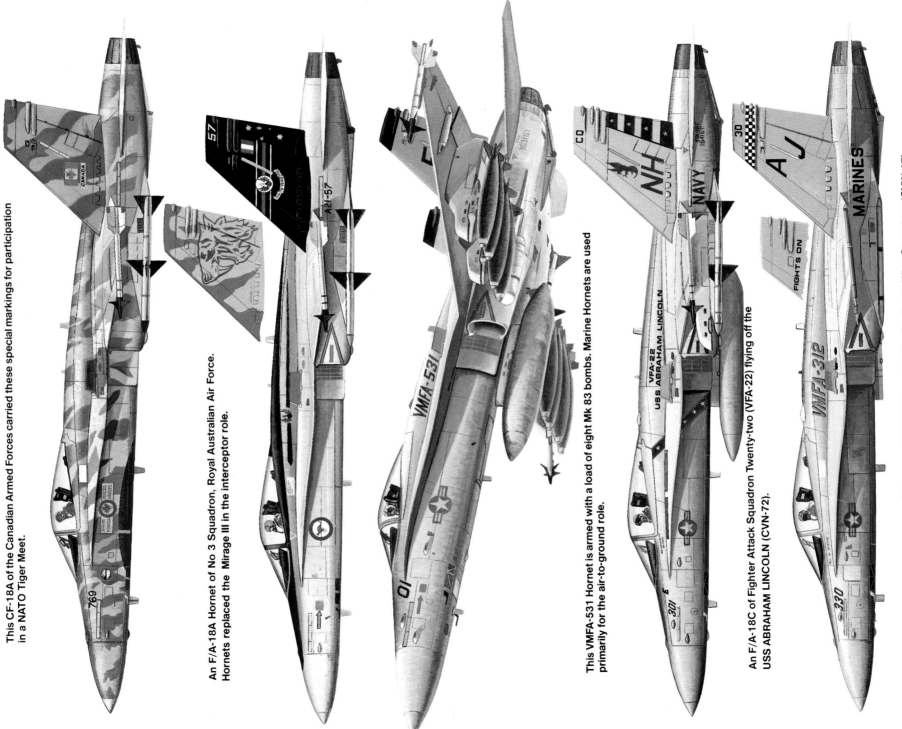

This CF-18A of the Canadian Armed Forces carried these special markings for participation in a NATO Tiger Meet.

An F/A-18A Hornet of No 3 Squadron, Royal Australian Air Force. Hornets replaced the Mirage III in the interceptor role.

This VMFA-531 Hornet is armed with a load of eight Mk 83 bombs. Marine Hornets are used primarily for the air-to-ground role.

An F/A-18C of Fighter Attack Squadron Twenty-two (VFA-22) flying off the USS ABRAHAM LINCOLN (CVN-72).

This Marine F/A-18C Hornet of VMFA-312 carried the Carrier Air Wing Seventeen (CVW-17) tail code for it's 1992 deployment aboard USS THEODORE ROOSEVELT.

This CF-18A Hornet (118769) was painted in this scheme for the Tiger Meet at RAF Fairford in July of 1991. The German-based Canadian Hornet squadrons share forty-three CF-18As and six CF-18Bs. (Richard Collens via Ted Carlson)

Some CF-18 Hornets of 410 Operational Conversion Unit, also known as the Cougar Squadron carried the silhouette of their mascot on the LEX fence. This CF-18B (188901) was visiting Edwards AFB on 18 October 1992. (Ted Carlson/Fotodynamics)

This CF-18 was painted in a special Red/White paint scheme with Gold lettering for the 50th anniversary of No 410 Cougar squadron. The scheme was carried for two weeks before the squadron commander ordered it removed.

A CF-18A of No 410 OCU on the ramp at Selfridge Air National Guard Base, Michigan on 18 July 1987. The AIM-9s on the wingtip rails were training rounds and were painted Blue to indicate their inert status. (D.F. Brown)

An F/A-18B Hornet of No 2 Operational Conversion Unit, Royal Australian Air Force, based at RAAF Williamtown. No. 2 OCU operates fourteen Hornets in the conversion training program. The fin flash was Yellow and Black with the squadron's Tiger head insignia on a Black disk.(McDonnell Douglas)

The 15 on the nose of this C-15 (F/A-18A) of the Spanish Air Force identifies this aircraft as being assigned to Ala de Caza (Fighter Wing) Fifteen at Zaragoza. The 22 is the individual aircraft number within the wing. The first Hornets were delivered to Spain during 1986. (Sergio Bottaro)

This CE-15 (F/A-18B) of the Spanish Air Force was the second Hornet delivered to Spain. Spain has ordered a total of twelve CE-15s and sixty C.15s (F/A-18As) to equip Ala de Caza 12 at Torrejon and Ala de Caza 15 at Zaragoza. (McDonnell-Douglas)

The first Hornet for the Kuwaiti Air Force was a F/A-18D two seat proficiency trainer, which made its first flight on 19 September 1991. The aircraft was delivered to Kuwaiti officials at St. Louis on 8 October 1991. (McDonnell-Douglas)

This Spanish Air Force C-15 (F/A-18A) carries the unit marking on the fin in Black. The serial C15-43 identifies this Hornet as the forty-third C-15 to be delivered to Spain. (Sergio Bottaro)

Kuwait will acquire some thirty-two F/A-18Cs and eight F/A-18Ds. These aircraft will be operated by a single unit, No 25 Squadron, Kuwaiti Air Force. The Kuwaiti Hornets were the first to be equipped with the newer more powerful F404-GE-402 engines. (McDonnell-Douglas)

Weapons

The F/A-18 is classified as a strike fighter and is capable of carrying a wide variety of ordnance on its nine external stations. These include:

Air-to-Air

An M-61 Vulcan 20MM cannon mounted in the nose, which is capable of firing up to 6,000 rounds per minute with a muzzle velocity of 3,400 feet per second. 570 rounds of 20MM are carried.

AIM-120 Advanced Medium Range Air-To-Air Missile (AMRAAM). The latest air-to-air missile in the U.S. inventory, the AMRAAM contains an active radar seeker, which allows the launching aircraft to "launch and leave" while the missile continues to home on the target. AMRAAMs will replace the AIM-7 Sparrow and will normally be carried on the fuselage stations (although it has been qualified for mounting on the wingtip stations). This missile can only be employed by the F/A-18C-D.

AIM-7F Sparrow. In production since 1951, the 500 pound Sparrow has been improved and modified to become a reliable radar-guided missile. The launching aircraft must continue to track the target aircraft throughout the flight of the missile in order to score. Employed by all versions of the Hornet.

AIM-9L/M Sidewinder. Also in production since 1951, the 200 pound Sidewinder is the most successful and copied air-to-air missile in history, with some thirty different versions. It is an all aspect heat-seeking missile, normally carried on the wingtip stations, although additional Sidewinders can be carried on the other wing pylons. Employed by all versions of the Hornet.

Air-to-Ground Missiles

AGM-62 WALLEYE. A 1,120 pound, unpowered, TV-guided missile which was manufactured during the Vietnam War and used in combat. The Walleye can only be carried on the outboard wing stations.

AGM-65 MAVERICK. Several versions of the Maverick have been produced, ranging in launch weight from 465 pounds to 665 pounds. Guidance is electro-optical or IR imaging and warhead size and types vary. All use the same rocket motor, and are launched from either LAU-88 or LAU-117 rails. IR versions can only be launched by the F/A-18C or F/A-18D.

AGM-84 HARPOON. A turbojet-powered 1,200 pound anti-ship missile which can only be carried on the outboard stations (2,3,5,6). Its inertial navigation system is pre-programmed to fly to the target area, where active radar guidance takes over for terminal guidance.

This pair of F/A-18Cs of VFA-82 display several of the possible weapons loads for the Hornet. Aircraft 100 is configured for the air-to-air mission, with six AIM-9 Sidewinders and a pair of AIM-7 Sparrows, while aircraft 314 carries eight Mk-84 bombs with nose plugs and tail fuzes for maximum penetration. (McDonnell-Douglas)

Hornet Guided Weapons
(Not To Scale)

Air-To-Air

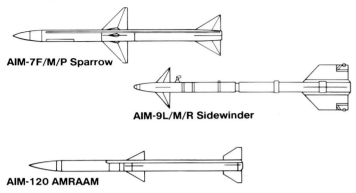

AIM-7F/M/P Sparrow

AIM-9L/M/R Sidewinder

AIM-120 AMRAAM

Air-To-Ground

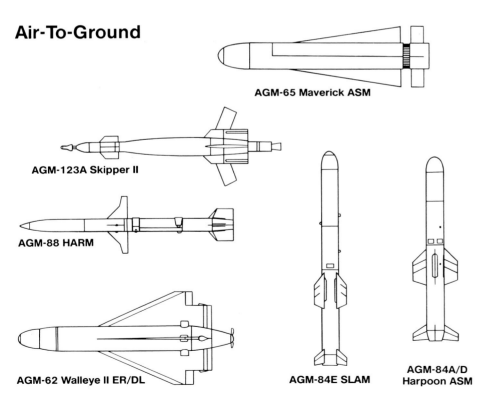

AGM-65 Maverick ASM

AGM-123A Skipper II

AGM-88 HARM

AGM-62 Walleye II ER/DL

AGM-84E SLAM

AGM-84A/D
Harpoon ASM

phase of the flight (up to fifty-five nautical miles). The Harpoon was also the basis for development of the Standoff Land Attack Missile (SLAM), which was first test fired from an F/A-18C on 21 October 1991. SLAM uses the Harpoon airframe and propulsion unit, Maverick IR imaging seeker, Walleye data link, and a Global Positioning System (GPS) receiver. Range is approximately the same as the Harpoon. When SLAM arrives in the target area, a video image of the target is transmitted to the launch aircraft and the pilot controls the terminal phase of flight. An operational test of SLAM was conducted in DESERT STORM, when an A-6 launched two missiles at a hardened Iraqi target. The first missile was used to breach the wall, and the second SLAM was flown through the resulting hole!

AGM-88 High Speed Anti-Radiation Missile (HARM). Used to attack SAM missile sites, the 800 pound, eleven nautical mile range HARM can be pre-programmed to attack known sites, or targets of opportunity with the AGM-88 seeker head homing on emitting enemy radars. HARM saw widespread and very effective use in the Gulf War. Can only be launched from outboard stations and is carried on LAU-118 rails.

AGM-123 SKIPPER II. A rocket powered version of the MK-83 Laser Guided Bomb (LGB) using a PAVEWAY II seeker head and the same rocket motor used by the AGM-45 Shrike. Designed to be launched from the A-6 and F/A-18.

An F/A-18A Hornet of the Naval Weapons Center, NAS China Lake, California, armed with a pair of AGM-84 Harpoon anti-ship missiles. The F/A-18 can only carry the Harpoon on the outboard wing stations. (McDonnell-Douglas)

Other Precision Guided Munitions (PGMs)

The Paveway series of Laser Guided bombs are the principle "smart bombs" used by all U.S. air arms. The seeker head is married to a variety of bomb bodies and fin combinations. These are as follows:

GBU-10, a 2,000 pound Mk 84 bomb with an MXU-600 short-wing fin kit. GBU-10A, a 2,000 pound Mk 84 bomb with an MXU-600A long-wing fin kit. GBU-10C/D/E/F, a 2,000 pound Mk 84 bomb with an MXU-651 folding-wing fin kit. GBU-12, a 500 pound Mk 82 bomb with MXU-602 short-wing fin kit. GBU-12A, a 500 pound Mk 82 bomb with MXU-602A long-wing fin kit. GBU-12B/C/D, a 500 pound Mk 82 bomb with MXU-650 fin kit. Laser-Guided-Bomb (LGB), a 1,000 pound Mk 83 bomb with MXU-641 long-wing fin kit. GBU-16A/B, a 1,000 pound Mk 83 bomb with MXU-667 fin kit.

Six different fuzes can be used with these bombs, ranging from short delay to instantaneous detonation.

General Purpose Bombs

MK 77 Mod 5 Fire Bomb (Napalm) recognizable by it's blunt, unpainted body (520 pounds).

This section of F/A-18Cs of VFA-86 are armed with Mk 82 Snakeye bombs on the wing stations and inert AIM-9 Sidewinders on the port wingtip station. Aircraft 413 also has an AIS instrumentation pod on the starboard wingtip station. (McDonnell-Douglas)

Air-To-Ground Weapons

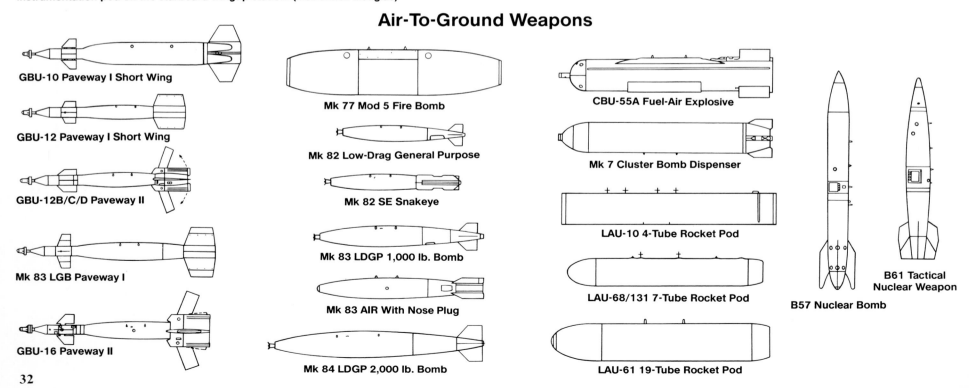

GBU-10 Paveway I Short Wing

GBU-12 Paveway I Short Wing

GBU-12B/C/D Paveway II

Mk 83 LGB Paveway I

GBU-16 Paveway II

Mk 77 Mod 5 Fire Bomb

Mk 82 Low-Drag General Purpose

Mk 82 SE Snakeye

Mk 83 LDGP 1,000 lb. Bomb

Mk 83 AIR With Nose Plug

Mk 84 LDGP 2,000 lb. Bomb

CBU-55A Fuel-Air Explosive

Mk 7 Cluster Bomb Dispenser

LAU-10 4-Tube Rocket Pod

LAU-68/131 7-Tube Rocket Pod

LAU-61 19-Tube Rocket Pod

B61 Tactical Nuclear Weapon

B57 Nuclear Bomb

Mk 82 Low Drag General Purpose (LDGP) 500 pound bomb with a streamlined conical fin (Mk-82 or BSU-33). The BLU-111 bomb uses the same bomb casing as all Mk 82 series bombs with a new explosive filler.

Mk 82 Snakeye 500 pound high drag bomb uses either a Mk 15 or BSU-86 Snakeye fin to retard the trajectory of the bomb, allowing the aircraft to clear the blast area.

Mk 83 LDGP 1,000 pound bomb uses Mk 83 conical fin. The BLU-110 bomb uses the same casing as all Mk 83 series, with new explosive filler.

Mk 83 AIR 1,000 pound high drag bomb uses BSU-85 air-inflatable retard fin assembly.

Mk 84 LDGP 2,000 pound bomb uses a Mk 84 conical fin.

Eight different fuzes can be used with these bombs including: short delay, proximity, instantaneous, or impact (among others). A nose plug is sometimes used with a tail fuze to provide for penetration of hardened shelters or underground bunkers.

Cluster Bomb Units (CBUs)

CBUs are used for area targets, such as troops and/or armor in the open, artillery or AAA and SAM sites. They contain bomblets which are loaded in a dispenser. The dispenser breaks apart in the air, scattering the bomblets over a large area. The area covered depends upon the altitude the dispenser is set to break apart and the number of bomblets. The Navy and Marines use the Mk-7 dispenser for the following CBUs:

Mk 20 Rockeye anti-armor CBU uses 247 Mk 118 bomblets (sub-munitions) and weighs 511 pounds at launch.

CBU-59 uses 717 BLU-77 anti-personnel mines and weighs 760 pounds at launch.

CBU-78 uses twenty-six BLU-91 anti-personnel mines and thirty-eight BLU-92 Gator anti-tank mines.

Fuel-Air Explosives

The operational premise of FAE is to mix fuel and air in the proper ratio to create explosions equal to 10 atmospheric pressures. This overpressure is useful for destroying underground complexes and detonating mine fields. FAEs use the SUU-49 dispenser to deploy three BLU-73 bomblets, whose fall is parachute retarded once released from the dispenser. The CBU-55A weighs 512 pounds and the CBU-72 weighs 522 pounds both are fitted with the Mk 339 fuze.

Unguided Rockets

5 INCH ZUNI: There are ten different types of warheads used in Zuni Rockets including: practice, GP, Anti-tank, Anti-Personnel, flare, smoke, incendiary and high explosive fragmentation. Zunis range in length from 95.1 inches (practice) to 115.4 inches (incendiary) and in weight from 108.7 pounds (anti-personnel) to 124 pounds (fragmentation). They are launched from reusable LAU-10 four shot rocket pods. They were widely used by USMC Fast FACs flying F/A-18Ds during DESERT STORM.

2.75 INCH: There are twenty different types of warheads used in these rockets. The Hornet carries them in the LAU-61 nineteen shot pod or the LAU-68/131 seven Shot pod. They range in length from 49.8 inches to 71 inches and in weight from 18.7 pounds to 30.1 pounds.

The armament load on this Hornet of VFA-305 includes an AGM-88 HARM on the outboard pylon, a CBU on the inboard pylon and the Mk 82 Snakeyes on a centerline VER. This load is highly unlikely for an actual mission, this aircraft was on static display at NAS Point Mugu 10 October 1992 for a base open house. (Ted Carlson/Fotodynamics)

An F/A-18A (BuNo 161761) of VFA-305 on the ramp at NAS Point Mugu on 6 July 1991. The aircraft is armed with AGM-88 HARM anti-radiation missiles and inert AIM-9 Sidewinder training rounds on the wingtips. (Ted Carlson/Fotodynamics)

Nuclear Weapons

The F/A-18 can carry two types of nuclear bombs, both on the fuselage centerline (station 5) only. They are:

The B57 was initially designed as a nuclear depth bomb, but was adopted for use as a low-yield tactical weapon using the BDU-12 shape. Delivery options are laydown or toss (loft) with ground or air burst. It weighs 500 pounds and has a yield of 5 to 20 kilotons.

The B61 is used as both strategic and tactical weapon nuke, using BDU-38 shape. It is delivered free-fall, retarded, laydown or toss, with surface or air burst. Weighs in at 710 pounds and yields 10 to 500 kilotons!

Pods

Although the following pods are not weapons in and of themselves, they are an integral part of the weapons delivery capability of the Hornet. They are carried on the fuselage stations in place of AIM-7 Sparrow missiles and include:

The Martin-Marietta AN/ASQ-173 Laser spot tracker/strike camera pod (LST/CAM) which is carried on the starboard fuselage station.

The Ford AN/AAS-38 forward looking infrared pod (FLIR) which is mounted on the port fuselage station.

The Hughes AN/AAR-50 Thermal Imaging Navigation Set (TINS). Normally mounted on the starboard fuselage station, it is used for the night attack mission.

A fuselage lateral stores station adaptor is required to mount these pods in place of AIM-7 or AIM-120 missiles.

The Ford AN/AAS-38 Forward Looking Infrared (FLIR) pod is carried on the port fuselage station replacing one of the AIM-7 Sparrows. It is six feet long and weighs 340 pounds. A pod adaptor is necessary to adapt the fuselage station for pod carriage. (Author)

This Marine Hornet is loaded with a total of twenty-eight Mk 82 Snakeye bombs. The wing stations carry Multiple Ejector Racks (MERs) each with six bombs while the centerline station has a MER with three bombs forward and one on the rear rack (the space between the rack and landing gear door is insufficient to allow for three bombs on the rear rack). (Robert Ward)

An F/A-18A (BuNo 162403) of VMFA-531 armed with Mk 82 bombs heads for the bombing range at San Clemente Island, California on 1 November 1990. VMFA-531 Gray Ghosts have since been decommissioned. (Ted Carlson/Fotodynamics)

War

"You're Carrying 4 Tons Of Explosives And People Are Shooting At You. No Problem. You're in an F/A-18 Hornet" (from a McDonnell Douglas advertisement).

The F/A-18 first saw action in March of 1986 as part of Operation PRARIE FIRE. The Libyan dictator, COL Muahmar Ghaddafi, was a chief sponsor of international terrorism and President Ronald Reagan was anxious to demonstrate to Ghaddafi the consequences of becoming the world's number one international outlaw. Under normal circumstances, terrorism is hard to pin on any one person, organization or country, unless they take credit for their actions, or are careless about covering their tracks.

Ghaddafi, in response to U.S. Sixth Fleet maneuvers in the Mediterranean Sea, had proclaimed the entire Gulf of Sidra as Libyan territorial waters and declared that anyone crossing his "Line of Death" which stretched across the Gulf from Tripoli to Benghazi, would be attacked. Since this proclamation was contrary to all international maritime law, the U.S. had only to defend itself in order to punish Libyan forces.

F/A-18 squadrons participating in PRARIE FIRE were all embarked in USS CORAL SEA (CV-43), which had gone to sea with an experimental air wing. The normal Navy air wing consists of two fighter squadrons (F-14s), a medium attack squadron (A-6s) and two light attack squadrons (A-7s). The CORAL SEA's air wing (CVW-13) had four squadrons of F/A-18s (VFA-131, VFA-132, VMFA-314 and VMFA-323) along with a squadron of A-6s (VA-55). Support units included VAW-127 (E-2Cs), VAQ-135 (EA-6Bs), VQ-2 (EA-3Bs) and HS-17 (SH-3Hs).

Early encounters with the Libyans were intercepts of Libyan MiG-23s, MiG-25s, Su-22s and Mirage F-1s. Although no shots were fired, the adrenaline level was still high. All naval aviators remembered the 1981 encounter with a pair of Libyan Su-22s, which unexpectedly fired on two VF-41 F-14s (much to their regret). The complete tactical domination displayed by Navy fighters caused the Libyan Air Force to become extremely timid in their approaches to American ships or aircraft and they played no part in the action that followed.

On 24 March 1986 shore-based SAM sites fired several missiles at American aircraft, all of which missed. As a result of these firings, A-7s and A-6s attacked the SAM sites, as well as several Libyan patrol boats. These attacks caused severe damage, with no U.S. casualties. It was an emphatic, but, as it turned out, unlearned lesson.

On 5 April 1986 a terrorist-planted bomb went off in a West Berlin disco, killing an American serviceman and a Turkish woman. It also injured seventy-nine American servicemen and 230 civilians. It was clearly aimed at the U.S. and it was easily traced to Ghaddafi. This attack led directly to Operation EL DORADO CANYON. Late in the evening of 14 April 1986, a combined strike force launched and headed for the Libyan coast, successfully attacking several military targets. F/A-18s attacked SAM sites with HARM missiles and, once again, there were no Navy casualties.

COL Ghaddafi's sponsorship of terrorism declined dramatically, due in large part to the fact that the USAF part of the raid was aimed at him personally. Although those bombs missed their target, the Libyan "mad dog of the Middle East," as President Reagan had dubbed him, got the message and lowered his profile.

Operation DESERT STORM

Four years later there was another mad dog on the loose in the Middle East. On 1

An F/A-18A of VMFA-314 traps aboard USS CORAL SEA (CV-43) on 29 January 1986, during operations in the Mediterranean. The Hornet was flying a CAP mission armed with AIM-9 Sidewinders and AIM-7 Sparrow missiles. It was during this period that the Sixth Fleet intercepted a number Libyan fighters probing its defenses. (Navy)

August 1990 Iraq, at the direction of President Saddam Hussein, invaded and occupied Kuwait, posing a clear and present danger to Saudi Arabia and a major portion of the world's oil reserves. Speaking of the invasion during the international furor that followed, President George Bush stated; "This will not stand!" He then went on to forge a coalition of twenty-eight nations to first shield Saudi Arabia, and then to eject Saddam from Kuwait.

Operation DESERT SHIELD began within days of the invasion. It was to become the greatest force buildup in the post-World War II world. Hundreds of thousands of troops and their equipment poured into the kingdom of Saudi Arabia. During the four years between the raids on Libya and DESERT SHIELD, the Hornet had become the light attack mainstay for both the Navy and Marines. 220 F/A-18 Hornets, from twenty-two squadrons, took part in DESERT SHIELD/DESERT STORM. They flew 11,000 combat sorties and accumulated over 30,000 hours of flight time. The mission capable rate of 90.4% contributed to the enviable record of no combat missions cancelled due to maintenance.

CVW-17 reported 128.5 flight hours for one Hornet during one month of the war. Only one Hornet was lost to enemy action and four Hornets returned safely to base after being hit by enemy fire. Of these, three were hit by surface-to-air missiles and the fourth was hit by AAA. One of those which returned safely flew the last thirty minutes back to base with no oil pressure! All four aircraft were returned to flight status within 48 hours. Operation DESERT STORM was the most lopsided victory in modern warfare. The fourth largest army in the world was bombed into submission and completely routed in a 100 hour ground war that saw its headlong retreat from Kuwait. The allied coalition was within a few weeks of total occupation of all of Iraq when the war was stopped. More than anything else, it was total vindication for the proponents of state-of-the-art modern air-power as embodied by aircraft such as the F/A-18 Hornet.

DESERT SHIELD/DESERT STORM
Hornet Squadrons

NAVY
CVW-5 USS MIDWAY (CV-41) Tail Code NF: VFA-151, VFA-192 and VFA-195. CVW-17 USS SARATOGA (CV-60) Tail Code AA: VFA-81 and VFA-83. CVW-1 USS AMERICA (CV-66) Tail Code AB: VFA-82 and VFA-86. CVW-8 USS THEODORE ROOSEVELT (CVN-71) Tail Code AJ: VFA-15 and VFA-87 CVW-14 USS INDEPENDENCE (CV-62) Tail Code NK: VFA-25 and VFA-113 (SHIELD only)
CVW-7 USS DWIGHT D. EISENHOWER (CVN-69) Tail Code AG: VFA-131 and VFA-136 (SHIELD only)

USMC
1st Marine Expeditionary Force, 3rd Marine Air Wing, MAG 11, SHEIKH ISA. VMFA(AW)-121 Tail Code VK, VMFA-212 Tail Code WD, VMFA-232 Tail Code WT, VMFA-314 Tail Code VW, VMFA-333 Tail Code DN and VMFA-451 Tail Code VM.

CANADIAN ARMED FORCES, DOHA, QATAR
Nos 409, 439 and 441 Squadrons.

This Hornet of VFA-131, armed with Mk-20 Rockeye cluster bombs, AIM-9 Sidewinders and AIM-7 Sparrows was positioned for launch from USS CORAL SEA (CV-43) on 22 March 1986 during operations against Libya as part of Operation EL DORADO CANYON. (Navy)

An F/A-18 of VFA-132 is given final checks by the Red Shirts (Ordnancemen) aboard USS CORAL SEA (CV-43). The Hornet is armed with an AGM-88A HARM anti-radiation missile. (U.S.Navy)

An F/A-18A Hornet of VMFA-314 Black Knights escorts a Libyan Arab Air Force MiG-25 Foxbat over the Gulf of Sidra. The MiG-25 was carrying AA-8 aphid dog fight missiles on the outboard wing pylons. (Navy)

This F/A-18A, is configured for a DESERT SHIELD combat air patrol with an additional Sparrow missile on the outboard wing pylon. The aircraft has its refueling probe deployed as it approaches a tanker during the long build-up period preceding DESERT STORM. (USAF)

COL Manfred 'Fokker' Rietsch commanded MAG-11, at Sheikh Isa during DESERT STORM. MAG-11 operated seven Marine Hornet squadrons, including the first squadron of night attack F/A-18Ds VMFA(AW)-121 to see combat. (D.F. Brown)

A bomb-laden Hornet plugs into a USAF KC-135 tanker prior to a DESERT STORM mission. The navigation problems facing pilots during DESERT STORM are evident from the trackless wastes of the Arabian Peninsula beneath the F/A-18. (USAF)

An F/A-18C of VFA-81 Sunliners forms up on a USAF tanker during a DESERT STORM bombing mission. VFA-81 scored the Navy's only DESERT STORM MiG kills, a pair of MiG-21s on the first day of the war. (USAF)

A VFA-83 F/A-18C Hornet gets the launch signal aboard the USS SARATOGA (CV-60) during DESERT STORM. The aircraft has the squadron designation painted on the centerline fuel tank. (Navy)

This F/A-18A of VMFA-451 Warlords is configured for a long range Combat Air Patrol mission armed with four AIM-7 Sparrows ad two AIM-9 Sidewinders. Marine units flew CAPs near the Iraqi border during DESERT SHIELD. (USAF)

LCDR. Mark Fox plugs into a KC-135 tanker during a DESERT STORM bombing mission. LCDR Fox scored a MiG-21 kill on 17 January 1991 while flying this F/A-18C of VFA-81, while carrying the same load, four Mk-84 2,000 pound bombs. (Navy)

This F/A-18C (BuNo 163502) was flown by LT Nick Mongillo when he scored a kill on an Iraqi Air Force MiG-21 Fishbed on the first day of DESERT STORM, 17 January 1991. He was able to engage and shoot down the MiG while still retaining his full bomb load. (D.F. Brown)

VMFA(AW)-121 flew night attack F/A-18Ds in the FAST FAC role during DESERT STORM, using four LAU-10 Zuni rocket pods to mark their targets with smoke for other Hornets to bomb. (USMC)

VFA-81 Hornets return from a DESERT STORM mission. Hornets flew over 11,000 combat missions, amounting to 30,000 combat hours, while achieving a mission capable rate of 91.5 percent during DESERT STORM. VFA-81 expended 1.36 million pounds of bombs and fifty-four HARM missiles. They suffered the only Hornet loss of the war on 17 January when LCDR Michael Speicher was shot down by an SA-6. (McDonnell-Douglas)

This F/A-18A of VMFA-314 carried its DESERT STORM kill markings back to MCAS El Toro after the war. The markings were carried in Black on the nose under the LEX. (D.F. Brown)

This F/A-18A (BuNo 162469 VW-03) of VMFA-314 returned to MCAS El Toro on 8 April 1991 still carrying its DESERT STORM kills score board under the cockpit. CAPT Day destroyed tanks, surface to air missile vehicles, guns and armored personnel carriers. (Ted Carlson/ Fotodynamics)

CAPT V.K. Mooney (call sign Slider) of VMFA-314 carried kill markings under the cockpit in Black that included tanks, mobile SAM batteries, armored personnel carriers, ships and artillery pieces. (D.F. Brown)

An F/A-18C Hornet of VMFA-232 at Marine Corps Air Station, Beaufort, S.C. immediately following the squadron's return to the U.S. after its deployment to Saudi Arabia for Operation DESERT STORM. (D.F.Brown)

Hornet Squadrons

As of January of 1993, the following Navy/Marine squadrons were equipped with the F/A-18 Hornet:

VFA-15 Valions NAS Cecil Field, Florida. Tail Code AJ. The squadron was established on 1 August 1968 as VA-15 with A-7s. Redesignated as VFA-15 on 1 October 1986. Currently assigned to CVW-8, aboard USS THEODORE ROOSEVELT with F/A-18Cs.

VFA-22 Fighting Redcocks NAS Lemoore, California. Tail Code NH. The squadron was established on 28 July 1948 and transitioned to the F/A-18 from A-7s. Currently assigned to CVW-11, aboard USS ABRAHAM LINCOLN.

VFA-25 Fist Of The Fleet NAS Lemoore, California. Tail Code NK. The squadron was established 1 January 1943. Redesignated as VFA-25, from VA-25, on 1 July 1983 and transitioned from A-7s to F/A-18A in November, 1983. Re-equipped with F/A-18Cs in 1991. Assigned to CVW-14.

VFA-27 Chargers NAS Lemoore, California. Tail Code NL, assigned to CVW-15 aboard USS KITTY HAWK. Transitioned to the F/A-18 from A-7s.

VFA-37 Bulls NAS Cecil Field, Florida. Tail Code AC. Assigned to CVW-3 aboard USS KENNEDY. Transitioned from A-7s and flew in Operation DESERT STORM.

VFA-81 Sunliners NAS Cecil Field, Florida. Tail Code AA. Assigned to CVW-17, USS SARATOGA. Transitioned from A-7s to F/A-18s on 4 February 1988. Flew missions in Operation DESERT STORM.

VFA-82 Marauders NAS Cecil Field, Florida. Tail Code AB. Assigned to CVW-1, USS AMERICA. Transitioned from A-7s on 15 July 1987. Flew missions in Operation DESERT STORM.

VFA-83 Rampagers NAS Cecil Field, Florida. Tail Code AA. Assigned to CVW-17, USS SARATOGA. Transitioned from A-7s on 1 February 1988. Flew missions in Operation DESERT STORM.

VFA-86 Sidewinders NAS Cecil Field, Florida. Tail Code AB. Assigned to CVW-1, USS KENNEDY.Transitioned from A-7s on 15 July 1987. Flew missions in Operation DESERT STORM.

VFA-87 Golden Warriors NAS Cecil Field, Florida. Tail Code AJ. Assigned to CVW-8, USS THEODORE ROOSEVELT. Transitioned from A-7s on 1 May 1986. Flew missions in Operation Desert Storm.

VFA-94 Mighty Shrikes NAS Lemoore, California. Tail Code NH. Assigned to CVW-11, USS ABRAHAM LINCOLN. Originally established as VA-94 on 26 March 1952 and transitioned to the F/A-18 from A-7s.

VFA-97 Warhawks NAS Lemoore, California. Tail Code NL. Assigned to CVW-15 aboard USS KITTY HAWK. Transitioned from A-7s.

VFA-105 Gunslingers NAS Cecil Field, Florida. Tail Code AC. Assigned to CVW-3, USS KENNEDY. Originally established as VA-105 with A-4s on 4 March 1968.

VFA-106 Gladiators NAS Cecil Field, Florida.Tail Code AD. The squadron was established 27 April 1984 as the East Coast training squadron. Has operated all versions of the Hornet. Also operates the Beech T-34C as a range aircraft.

VFA-113 Stingers NAS Lemoore, California. Tail Code NK. Assigned to CVW-14, USS CARL VINSON. The squadron was established as VF-113 on 15 July 1948. Transitioned from A-7s on 25 March 1983 as one of the first two Navy F/A-18 squadrons. Flew missions in Operation DESERT STORM.

VFA-125 Rough Riders NAS Lemoore, California. Tail Code NJ. The squadron was established 13 November 1980 as the West Coast Hornet training squadron. It was also

An F/A-18C (BuNo 164039) NH 301 of VFA-22 Fighting Redcocks returns to Nellis AFB after a Desert Flag mission 8 April 1992. NH 301 was assigned to the squadron commander and carries the logo CO on the fin tip in Black. (Ted Carlson/Fotodynamics)

This new production night attack F/A-18C (BuNo 163766) was assigned to VFA-25 Fist of the Fleet. The aircraft was visiting MCAS El Toro on 12 July 1992. The aircraft carries its ship assignment, USS INDEPENDENCE, on the fin tip in Black. (Ted Carlson/Fotodynamics)

the first operational Hornet squadron. It operates all types of F/A-18s, as well as the Beech T-34C Mentor as a range clearing aircraft.

VFA-127 Cylons NAS Fallon, Nevada. Tail Code NJ. The first adversary squadron to operate the Hornet. Transitioned to the F/A-18A/B from Northrop F-5s in 1992.

VFA-131 Wildcats NAS Cecil Field, Florida. Tail Code AG. Assigned to CVW-7, USS Dwight D. Eisenhower. The squadron was established on 3 October 1983 as a new F/A-18 squadron. Flew missions against Libya in Operations PRARIE FIRE and EL DORADO CANYON in March and April 1986.

VFA-132 Privateers NAS Lemoore, California. Tail Code AE. The squadron was established on 3 January 1984 as a new F/A-18 squadron. Flew missions against Libya in March and April 1986 aboard USS CORAL SEA while assigned to CVW-13. Flew with CVW-6, USS FORRESTAL in 1991. Disestablished 1 June 1992.

VFA-136 Knighthawks NAS Cecil Field, Florida. Tail Code AG. The squadron was established on 1 July 1985 as a new F/A-18 squadron. Assigned to CVW-7, USS DWIGHT D. EISENHOWER.

VFA-137 Kestrels NAS Lemoore, California. Tail Code NE. The squadron was established 1 July 1985 as a new F/A-18 squadron. Transferred from CVW-6, USS FORRESTAL, to CVW-2, USS RANGER in 1992.

VFA-146 Blue Diamonds NAS Lemoore, California. Tail Code NG. The squadron was established 1 February 1946 as VA-46. Operated A-4 and A-7 before transition to the F/A-18C. Assigned to CVW-9 aboard USS NIMITZ.

VFA-147 Argonauts NAS Lemoore, California. Tail Code NG. The squadron was established 1 February 1967 as VA-147, the first fleet A-7 squadron. Transitioned to the Hornet in 1989.

VFA-151 Vigilantes NAS Lemoore, California. Tail Code NE. Originally established as VF-23 on 6 August 1948, became VF-151 on 23 February 1959. Transitioned from F-4 Phantoms on 1 June 1986, tail coded NF and based at NAF Atsugi, Japan and with CVW-5 aboard USS MIDWAY. Reassigned to Lemoore when MIDWAY was retired. Assigned

to CVW-2 on USS RANGER.

VFA-161 Chargers NAS Lemoore, California. Tail Code NM. Transitioned from F-4S to F/A-18, October 1986. Disestablished 1 April 1987, prior to deployment with CVW-10 on USS NIMITZ.

VFA-192 Golden Dragons NAF Atsugi, Japan. Tail Code NF. Transitioned from A-7s at NAS Lemoore 10 January 1985, moved to Atsugi in November 1986, flying from USS MIDWAY (home ported at Yokosuka). Currently flying F/A-18C with CVW-5 aboard USS INDEPENDENCE.

VFA-195 Dambusters NAF Atsugi, Japan. Tail Code NF. Transitioned from A-7s at NAS Lemoore 10 January 1985, moved to Atsugi in November 1986, flying from USS MIDWAY. Currently flying F/A-18C with CVW-5 on USS INDEPENDENCE.

VFA-203 Blue Dolphins NAS Cecil Field, Florida. Tail Code AF. The squadron was established originally on 1 July 1970 at Cecil. Transitioned to F/A-18A from A-7 Corsairs in March 1991 and assigned to CVW-20. Third reserve squadron to fly the Hornet.

VFA-204 River Rattlers NAF New Orleans, Louisiana. Tail Code AF. The squadron was established originally on 1 July 1970 at NAS Cecil. Transitioned to F/A-18A from A-7 Corsair.

VFA-303 Goldenhawks NAS Lemoore, California. Tail Code ND. The squadron was established 1 July 1970 as the first reserve squadron to fly the A-7 Corsair II. Redesignated VFA-303 on 1 January 1984 as the first reserve squadron to fly the F/A-18.

VFA-305 Lobos NAS Point Mugu, California. Tail Code ND. The squadron was established 1 July 1970 and transitioned to the F/A-18 on 18 January 1987 as the second Hornet reserve squadron.

VX-4 Evaluators NAS Point Mugu, California. Tail Code XV. Involved with testing of the Hornet since 1981.

VX-5 Vampires NWC China Lake, California. Tail Code XE. Has been testing Hornets since 1981.

Strike Warfare Center NAS Fallon, Nevada. No tail code, carries a lightning bolt on

An F/A-18C (BuNo 164240) of VFA-37 Bulls lands at El Centro NAF during January of 1992 for a period of weapons training. The squadron logo on the fuselage is unusual in that it is much smaller than usually found on Navy Hornet squadrons. (M.Gapski via Ted Carlson)

The Rampagers assigned this aircraft to be the squadron's CAG bird. It carried the CVW-1 badge on the port side of the vertical fin and a Battle E award painted on the fuselage just behind the cockpit. (D.F. Brown)

the fin of its F/A-18s.

Strike Aircraft Test Directorate NAS Patuxent River, Maryland. Tail Code 7T.

United State Naval Test Pilot School, NAS Patuxent River, Maryland. Tail Code USNTPS.

Pacific Missile Test Center NAS Point Mugu, California. PMTC on tail.

Naval Weapons Center NAS China Lake, California. Tail Code Eagle with anchor and two missiles.

NASA Ames/Dryden Flight Research Center, Edwards AFB, California. Received some prototype F/A-18s, which have been used for high angle of attack (AOA) research and chase duties. No tail code.

Blue Angels. The Navy Air Demonstration Squadron, NAS Pensacola, Florida. Transitioned to the Hornet from A-4F in 1986. The team operates eight F/A-18As and one F/A-18B, all early models with the gun removed and software optimised for aerobatics. Non-combat qualified.

VMFAT-101 Sharpshooters MCAS El Toro, California. Tail Code SH. Transitioned from F-4s at Yuma to Hornets at El Toro on 1 October 1987. As the Marine Corps fleet replacement training squadron for the F/A-18, it operates all models of the Hornet, as well as a few Beech T-34C Mentors for proficiency training.

VMFA-112 Cowboys NAS Dallas, Texas. Tail Code MA. Transitioned to the F/A-18 in 1992. It was the last squadron of Naval Aviators to operate the F-4 Phantom, which it had flown since 1976.

VMFA-115 Silver Eagles MCAS Beaufort, South Carolina. MAG-31 Tail Code VE. Transitioned to the Hornet from F-4S in 1985. Flew missions in Operation DESERT STORM.

VMFA-122 Crusaders MCAS Beaufort, South Carolina. MAG-31 Tail Code DC. Transitioned from the F-4S in 1986. It was the second east coast F/A-18 Marine Corps squadron. It has carried the same tail code and cross-on-shield markings since it flew FJ Furies in the 1950s.

VMFA-134 Smokes MCAS El Toro, California. Tail Code MF. A Marine Reserve squadron, assigned to MAG-46 in Atlanta, Georgia.

VMFA-142 Flying Gators NAS Cecil Field, Florida. Transitioned from A-4 Skyhawks after being redesignated from VMA-142. Reserve squadron assigned to MAG-42.

VMFA-212 Lancers MCAS Kaneohe Bay, Hawaii MAG-24. Tail Code WD. Transitioned from the F-4S to the Hornet in 1989. First USMC squadron to operate the F/A-18C.

VMFA-232 Red Devils MCAS Kaneohe Bay, Hawaii MAG-24. Tail Code WT. Transitioned from the F-4S to the F/A-18C in 1989. Flew DESERT STORM missions from Bahrain.

VMFA-235 Death Angels MCAS Kaneohe Bay, Hawaii MAG-24. Tail Code DB. Transitioned from the F-4S in 1989.

VMFA-251 Thunderbolts MCAS Beaufort, South Carolina MAG-31. Tail Code DW. The third east coast Hornet squadron, transitioned from the F-4 in 1986.

VMFA-312 Checkerboards MCAS Beaufort, South Carolina MAG-31. Transitioned from F-4S in 1988.

VMFA-314 Black Knights MCAS El Toro, California MAG-11. Tail Code DR. Transitioned from the F-4 in 1983. Went aboard USS CORAL SEA (CV-43) for 1986 cruise and saw combat in Operations PRARIE FIRE and EL DORADO CANYON flying missions against Libya.

VMFA-321 Hell's Angels NAF Washington, D.C. MAG-41. Tail Code MG. Transitioned from F-4S in 1991. Reserve Squadron with a long history, dating from F-8 Crusaders in the 1970s.

A pair of F/A-18Cs of VFA-86 Sidewinders on the ramp at NAS Miramar. The rattlesnake on the fin is in Black and Gray, the aircraft number on the fin tip is in White, while all other markings are in Black. (TEd Carlson/Fotodynamics)

An F/A-18A (BuNo 163103) of VFA-87 on final approach for landing at Marine Corps Air Station El Toro on 12 June 1992. The Indian head on the fin, Navy and national insignia are in Dark Gray, while all numbers on the aircraft are in Black. (Ted Carlson/Fotodynamics)

VMFA-323 Death Rattlers MCAS El Toro, California MAG-11. Tail Code WS. Transitioned from the F-4 in 1983. Went aboard USS CORAL SEA (CV-43) for 1986 cruise and saw combat against Libya.

VMFA-333 Shamrocks MCAS Beaufort, South Carolina MAG-31. Tail Code DN. Transitioned to the Hornet from F-4S in 1987. Flew missions in Operation DESERT STORM. Disestablished on 31 March 1992.

VMFA-451 Warlords MCAS Beaufort, South Carolina MAG-31. Tail Code VM. Transitioned from the F-4S in 1987. Deployed aboard USS CORAL SEA as part of CVW-13 in 1989.

VMFA-531 Gray Ghosts MCAS El Toro, California MAG-11. Tail Code EC. Transitioned from the F-4N to F/A-18A in 1983. Decommissioned in 1992.

VMFA(AW)-121 Green Knights MCAS El Toro, California MAG-11. Tail Code VK. The first Marine Corps squadron to operate the F/A-18D night attack Hornet. Flew Fast FAC and Night Interdiction missions in Operation DESERT STORM.

VMFA(AW)-225 Vagabonds MCAS El Toro, California MAG-11. Tail Code CE. Became the third Marine Corps squadron the fly the night attack F/A-18D when it was recommissioned on 1 July 1991, after retiring the A-6 Intruder on 30 June 1991.

VMFA(AW)-242 Bats MCAS El Toro, California MAG-11. Tail Code DT. The unit transitioned from the A-6E Intruder in 1990.

This F/A-18A of VFA-136 Kestrels on the ramp at Andrews AFB during March of 1989. VFA-136 carried their carrier assignment, USS DWIGHT D. EISENHOWER, under the fuselage NAVY logo. The aircraft is unusual in that it carries the unit insignia on the fin in Black instead of Gray. (D.F. Brown)

This F/A-18C (BuNo 164685) night attack Hornet of VFA-113 Stingers on approach to runway 34R at MCAS El Toro on 25 September 1992. The unit carries their carrier assignment, USS CARL VINSON, on the fin in Black. (Ted Carlson/Photodynamics)

This F/A-18A of VFA-132 was assigned to USS FORRESTAL before CV-59 became the training carrier for the Navy. VFA-132 had one of the most unusual color schemes of any Hornet squadron with all numbers and lettering in a script style. (D.F. Brown)

VFA-151's CAG bird (Commander Air Wing Five, CVW-5) carried the squadron patch in full color on the fin. The squadron was flying from USS MIDWAY while the ship operated out of Japan during December of 1989. (Shinichi Ohtaki)

VFA-132 Privateers changed their color scheme when they changed carriers. They went back to the block style lettering and now featured the figure of a pirate on the fin in Gray. The unit was assigned to USS Coral Sea (CV-43) in March of 1989. (D.F. Brown)

This F/A-18A (BuNo 161926) of VFA-203 Blue Dolphins carries a special two-tone Gray camouflage scheme for use in the aggressor role. The aircraft was on the ramp at NAS Miramar on 5 December 1992. (Ted Carlson/Fotodynamics)

This F/A-18C (BuNo 162848) of VFA-137 on approach to MCAS El Toro on 18 December 1992 wa s assigned as the CAG aircraft (aircraft 400) and has a high visibility color scheme with full color unit markings on the fin and all lettering in Black. (Ted Carlson/Fotodynamics)

An F/A-18A (BuNo 162462) of VMFA-115 on the ramp at Andrews Air Force Base, outside Washington, D.C. on December 1986. The light colored stripes on the fin and fuselage are low light level strip formation lights. (D.F. Brown)

An F/A-18A (BuNo 161737) of VFA-303 returns to Nellis Air Force Base, Nevada on 11 October 1989 after flying a air combat maneuvering (ACM) mission against the 57th Fighter Weapons Wing Aggressors. The aircraft carries inert AIM-9s on the wingtip stations. (Ted Carlson/Fotodynamics)

An F/A-18C of VMFA-235 Death Angels on the ramp MCAS Beaufort, South Carolina shortly after the squadron returned from Operation DESERT STORM during 1991. The aircraft is carrying a travel pod on the outboard wing station. (D.F.Brown)

Carrying an inert training AIM-9 Sidewinder on the starboard wingtip station, an F/A-18C (BuNo 163725) of VMFA-212 makes its final approach for landing at MCAS Yuma on 18 October 1990. (Ted Carlson/Fotodynamics)

This F/A-18C (BuNo 163723) of VMFA 232 is configured with three 330 gallon external tanks. The aircraft was home based at MCAS Kaneohe Bay, Hawaii, and was visiting MCAS El Toro on 24 July 1992. (Ted Carlson/Photodynamics)

This F/A-18A of VMFA-251 on the ramp at Selfridge ANGB in July of 1987 was visiting the base to take part in Exercise SENTRY WOLVERINE. The pilot has hung his anti-G suit from the port sidewinder launch rail while he does the pre-flight walk-around. (D.F. Brown)

An F/A-18C of VMFA-312 Checkertails on the flight line of NAS Oceana, Virginia during April of 1992 has full color markings and is carrying an air combat maneuvering range instrumentation pod on the wingtip station. (D.F. Brown)

The F/A-18As of VMFA-321 Hell's Angels are home based at Naval Air Facility Washington (Andrews AFB). This FA-18C (BuNo 161981) was on approach to MCAS El Toro for a training visit on 17 August 1992. (Ted Carlson/Photodynamics)

Carrying the tailcode for USS KITTY HAWK (CV-63) this F/A-18A (BuNo 163100) of VMFA-314 begins its final for MCAS El Toro 2 October 1992. This aircraft had been formerly assigned to VFA-87 Golden Warriors. (Ted Carlson/Fotodynamics)

The retractable pilots boarding ladder on this F/A-18C of VMFA-451 Warlords is deployed and the canopy is raised ready for the pilot to man his aircraft, at MCAS Beaufort, S.C. This was the 500th Hornet off the production line (D.F. Brown)

The Warlords were the first East Coast Marine Hornet squadron to deploy aboard a carrier. The squadron went aboard USS CORAL SEA (CV-43) as part of CVW-13 during 1989 and carried the air wing's AK tailcode on the rudder.(D.F. Brown)

This F/A-18A of VMFA-333 Shamrocks on the ramp at MCAS Beaufort, S.C. shortly after the squadron returned from DESERT STORM during 1991 has a FLIR pod mounted in the port fuselage station, a standard fitting for aircraft engaged in the air-to-ground mission. (D.F. Brown)

Blue Angel Number 7 is an F/A-18B Hornet usually flown by the team announcer and used to for VIP and press rides. The team has a total of eight F/A-18As and one F/A-18B. All aircraft have had the M61 cannon removed. (D.F. Brown)

Blue Angel Number One is an early production F/A-18A (BuNo 161973) retrofitted with the LEX fence. Blue Angels Hornets have been modified (special software) for air show work and are no longer combat capable. (D.F. Brown)

Aircraft Of The U.S. Navy

1060

1062

1065

1082

1100

1103

1105

1119

1120

squadron/signal publications